The Whole Truth

Rosalind Coward was born in south London where she currently lives with her partner and children. She studied at New Hall, Cambridge, and at the Centre for Contemporary Cultural Studies, Birmingham. She has contributed to numerous journals and newspapers, as well as appearing regularly on television. She has taught in British universities and is now working as a freelance writer.

Her previous books include *Patriarchal Precedents*, *Language and Materialism* (with John Ellis), and her bestseller, *Female Desire*. Faber and Faber first published *The Whole Truth* in hardback in 1989 and it provided the ideas for a BBC documentary, *Natural Movements by the same author*

FEMALE DESIRE (Paladin)
PATRIARCHAL PRECEDENTS (Routledge)
LANGUAGE AND MATERIALISM
with John Ellis (Routledge)

The Whole Truth
The Myth of Alternative Health

Rosalind Coward

faber and faber

LONDON · BOSTON

First published in 1989
by Faber and Faber Limited
3 Queen Square London WC1N 3AU
This paperback edition first published in 1990

Photoset by Wilmaset, Birkenhead, Wirral
Printed in Great Britain by
Cox & Wyman Ltd, Reading, Berkshire

A CIP record for this book is
available from the British Library

ISBN 0–571–15222–8

Contents

Acknowledgement

I would like to thank Neil McDonald for his invaluable help.

Introduction

Who could have foreseen, fifteen years ago, the current popularity of 'alternative' therapies with all that they imply about attitudes towards health, the body and the emotions? There was nothing to indicate that the 1980s would see an extraordinary proliferation of so-called fringe therapies. Who could have foretold that reflexology, aromatherapy and the Alexander technique would no longer be the pastimes of cranks but treatments for bodily and mental well-being recognized by large sectors of the population? Or that it would become a commonplace for people to explain their attraction to these therapies on the grounds that they attend to 'physical, mental and spiritual well-being'. Fifteen years ago we might have seemed like the confident inheritors of a 'rationalist' society. Not only were superstitions firmly banished to the fringes, but even the more sober, rationalist Anglican religion seemed set on an irreversible decline. 'Spiritual' was a term used, and received, with embarrassment. Science would govern our understanding and explanation of the physical world. And nowhere was this clearer than in attitudes towards the body and health, the very area which has now suffered such a total reversal.

In the 1950s and 1960s, the concerns about health and the body were very different from our own current obsessions. Then was a period of basic optimism in the medical establishment. Most infectious diseases were under control; indeed an effective vaccine against poliomyelitis seemed to spell the definitive end to disastrous epidemics. Improved hygiene, the triumph of medical cures and developments in surgical techniques, suggested that very few illnesses would be without any kind of treatment. And, in Britain at least, health was a 'right', for the first time available to the ordinary person. If you became ill the services were there, and the possibilities for cure or treatment were open to all. Of course, there were always the incurable diseases like cancer, the subject of immense taboos. But even here the medical establishment could be heard confidently predicting that it was only a matter of time. It appeared that the medical profession possessed known and tried treatments for most illnesses and diseases. What was not fully understood was being researched.

Paradoxically, though, people appeared to be more fatalistic. Some chronic diseases seemed unlikely to disappear and most people recognized the limitations of medical science. But even here Western society was prepared to congratulate itself. It could boast an extensive and apparently humane infrastructure of general practice, and hospital care to cope with nursing those who could not be cured. There were drugs to alleviate the worst suffering. In fact, confidence in the medical profession could not have been higher, as was clear from the endless medical soap operas on the television in the 1960s. The medical profession was where the human body was known and understood and people could entrust their bodies to it with complete confidence, as they might entrust a machine to an expert mechanic. The doctor was intelligent, respectable and caring, symbolizing all that was best in 'professionalism', a term which had none of the pejorative connotations of today.

For most people, health was something which only became an issue when they were ill. Health and illness were beyond control. Health was something dispensed by the doctor. Illness was down to chance – either in the form of contact with an external virus or some genetic predisposition to a particular disease. Of course there was a general commonsense view that people had to protect their health. The war had raised general consciousness of the need for good nutrition. But what was almost completely absent in that period was anything like the sense of good health as an optimum state of well-being which prevails now, where we are told that health is not in the hands of the doctor but our own responsibility. Nor was there previously any sense that health was a positive category, something in which we are told to play an active role and something which might even require 'shopping around' until we found an appropriate therapy.

Of course there were always groups who challenged the scientific orthodoxy and viewed the body, and the individual's role in health and illness differently. Herbalism and homoeopathy are old-established practices, offering quite different forms of treatment from the medical establishment. In fact most of the alternative therapies currently enjoying vogue are based on ideas originating somewhere in between the 1880s and the 1930s. But all these views had the stigma of 'unorthodox' and carried connotations of the unscientific or mystical. What they had to say about the body and health was regarded as belief rather than science and they were relegated firmly to the fringe. They were seen as the dubious inheritors of Victorian dabbling in spiritualism and the paranormal, last vestiges of mystical, irrational and deluded ways of seeing the world. Even the popularity of transcendental meditation in the 1960s as a way of reaching well-being did nothing to move such views out of the fringes. Transcendental meditation was seen as part of the hippie drug culture and had nothing to do with how most people viewed health.

Nothing could present a more startling difference to the picture today. Suddenly 'cranky' ideas like Rudolph Steiner's anthroposophical medicine are seen as respectable precursors of holistic medicine. Herbalism and homoeopathy have won widespread respect. On the back of a massive interest in relaxation techniques, transcendental meditation is widely recognized as a useful health aid. So-called fringe practices, ranging from yoga through to herbalism, reflexology and psychotherapy are activities and practices now met by virtually everyone. Indeed a recent survey revealed that between 1984 and 1987, 34 per cent of the population tried an alternative therapy. Although some claim that interest in these therapies has been growing steadily for the last twenty-five years, most practitioners describe an explosion of interest over the last ten years: 'Although reliable information has only recently become available, it is generally agreed that over the last five to ten years public and professional interest in this field has increased considerably.'[1] Indeed it hard not to be aware of these therapies. There are television programmes about them. Radio stations and magazines have their alternative medicine experts. Publishers, awed by the success of Thorsons, the specialist publishers of alternative health books, are now hastily publishing on naturopathy, reflexology and so on.

This is more than an increased tolerance for 'fringe' activities. It shows that large sectors of the population are prepared to take alternative therapies seriously as a way of becoming or staying well. There must be very few of us who don't have at least one acquaintance doing some alternative therapy, if not someone who is a fully paid-up convert. It is a quiet revolution. At a moment when, in Britain at least, politicians struggle over the extent to which the health services should be privatized, vast numbers of the population are already paying up willingly for practitioners to deal with our health differently. The widespread acceptance of alternative therapies marks profound changes in attitudes towards health and the body. These changes are so radical that individuals are positively seeking out approaches where the expertise of the medical establishment is at best irrelevant, and at worst the preachings of the devil, and where mentions of the spiritual dimension of health not only do not deter customers but positively attract them.

How are we to account for this dramatic change in public attitudes? How are we to account for this new ideal of optimum and permanent good health which it is suddenly our personal responsibility to pursue? And how do we explain the sudden popularity of these activities which would have been the subject of jokes and exclusions such a short time ago? These are the questions which form the subject of this book, and not the question of whether alternative therapies work. What interests me is why these views have become so popular. What has happened to make people think that these new practices offer a surer way to health than the orthodox and scientific views of conventional medicine? What is it that these therapies offer to do, and what is it that they explain to individuals, that makes them so attractive? My contention is that alternative therapies are based on a new philosophy of the body, health, and nature, a new philosophy which has somehow managed to capture or echo popular consciousness. I make no attempt to research claims for the efficacy of alternative medicine, but instead I try to 'unpick' the meanings which cluster around this new philosophy.

These philosophical shifts are far more significant than whether or not a particular therapy 'works'. For at the centre of these changes are new concepts of nature, health, the body and the individual's role in health. Through these new representations of the body, we are all being encouraged to develop a much more loaded sense of good health and well-being, one which touches deeply on ourselves as individuals. Notions of what we are as people, individuals or bodies, and what our relationship is with nature, have profound effects on our self-perceptions and the kind of decisions which will get made at personal and social levels. Although these philosophical shifts may not seem important at first, they are having a significant impact on social consciousness. I want to understand why these shifts around notions of health, nature and individuality have taken place. In particular I am interested in the implications these new views have for how people think of themselves socially and politically.

In this book I have grouped together various therapies and practices who will make uncomfortable bedmates. Long-standing practitioners of homoeopathy will not be overjoyed to find themselves grouped with the sellers of Pulsor crystals. Within alternative therapies themselves there are strong divisions over the more 'mystical' or 'spiritual' elements. Many practitioners do not want to be grouped with therapies where these elements are central. Indeed, I spoke to several practitioners, particularly of therapies like homoeopathy and acupuncture, who themselves referred to 'fringe' therapies which they saw as being more like religions than medicines. Some of these practitioners prefer to see themselves as complementing orthodox medicine, providing techniques and a knowledge of the body which are missing from orthodox medicine. I have grouped all the alternative therapies together not to be critical of them in any dismissive way. Indeed I have used alternative medicines and feel sympathetic to some of their practices and ideas. But many of the fundamental tenets of these therapies seem so similar that it is difficult to drive a definite line between the 'respectable' and the 'fringe' therapies. What is more, I believe the same impetus underlies the popularity of *all* the alternative therapies. And, in trying to understand this impetus and what it means, I have stressed points in common rather than differences.

This is a difficult book to write because it is an archaeology of the present. I am attempting to excavate the roots of, and reasons for, major shifts in people's *contemporary* perceptions of themselves and this presents problems not encountered in looking at a period way back in the past. Examining the present represents an attempt to decipher the meanings of a belief system at the point where it is still emerging and gaining a hold. It is particularly difficult in the case of alternative therapies because in so many ways they appear to be 'radical', criticizing some of the more deadening aspects of contemporary society. This radical edge makes me loath to appear too critical. Yet it seems important that we should understand this phenomenon by which the meanings of health and individual responsibility are being so drastically transformed. For I am convinced that these changed views of health are at the spearhead of general changes in ideas about the individual's role in society, ideas which will have enormous consequences for how much an individual feels he or she should change or accept society as it is.

In this book I treat alternative therapies both as a spearhead *and* as a symptom of widespread changes in attitudes. Alternative therapies seem to be a sort of avant-garde for new ideas about health and the body. Simultaneously these therapies are themselves symptomatic of much wider changes. Many people, especially the practitioners, would be surprised to hear alternative therapies represented in this way. As far as they are concerned the success of alternative therapies can be understood almost entirely in terms of the failures and inadequacies of conventional medicine. Most alternative practitioners explain their current popularity as the result of their promise to be truly *alternative* approaches to illness and health. Yet, as will become apparent, the forces which attract many people to alternative therapies go way beyond a discontent with conventional medicine. More often than not individuals are attracted to the new mythology about nature and health which surrounds these practices.

Obviously dissatisfaction with orthodox medicine's approach to health has been important in fuelling the alternative health movement and the criticisms of orthodox medicine have to be taken seriously. There is a sense that conventional medicine has failed to deliver what it promised, that is, good health for the population. In spite of its triumphalist claims, conventional medicine has had little success with chronic and degenerative diseases like cancer and heart disease. Indeed, these appear to be on the increase. What is more, the treatment which people are offered has been criticized as being, in some cases, as good as useless. Thus, in the treatment of advanced cancer, drugs and certain forms of treatment (surgery and chemotherapy for instance) are increasingly seen as both ineffective and incredibly stressful for the individual. Survival rates apparently differ little whether or not the individual submits to orthodox treatment. The only difference is that the individual who does submit often has to live with some extremely unpleasant side effects.

These side effects are an important focus of the criticism made by the alternative therapies. Again, the movement sees itself as articulating the growing discontent which the public feel with their treatment. For not only has conventional medicine 'failed' in its promises, but it is now actually seen as 'endangering' people's health. Those within the alternative therapies movement cite several major scandals involving the use of dangerous drugs, like thalidomide; people, they say, are now aware that profit sometimes seems more important than health in conventional medicine. But it is not just profit which is blamed; there is a belief that the use of 'high tech' and drug-based medicine is the product of a particular way of viewing sickness. Conventional medicine, they argue, insists on only treating the disease or symptom. Thus, with cancer, conventional medicine will concentrate on the tumour and attempt to eradicate it, paying little attention to the presence of whatever produced the cancer within the overall system of the body. For alternative therapists, this approach is seen as the reason for some of the inhuman attitudes discovered within conventional medicine; the eradication of the symptom appears more important than the overall comfort of the individual who may well be near the end of their life anyway.

These critiques of conventional medicine waver between a sense of its failure to deliver real health and anger at the unnecessary suffering which individuals have been put through in the course of a supposed cure. The British Medical Association, in a report entirely unsympathetic to alternative medicine, represented these criticisms as a sort of greed whereby the successes of conventional medicine had made people expect the eradication of all suffering, something which conventional medicine cannot offer. 'It is particularly interesting that these criticisms of medicine should appear at a time when the great modern developments in rational therapeutics and in diagnostic techniques have revolutionized effective treatment of many diseases, and since the nineteen fifties have greatly enhanced our expectation of medical science.'[2] In other words the medical establishment attributed discontent to the very 'successes' of orthodox medicine in raising expectation. However, this report, which embodied the views of the medical orthodoxy, failed to take on board the other elements fundamental to the critique of conventional medicine by its alternatives. In particular there was scant attention paid to criticisms of inhumanity and the inducement of unnecessary suffering. Yet adherents to alternative medicine cite their own 'gentleness' and use of 'natural' substances – the opposite of conventional medicine – as a principal reason in attracting newcomers.

Even if all people accepted that certain illnesses could not be dealt with by conventional medicine, alternative therapies would still be able to make a convincing case that the medical infrastructure, so much the pride and joy of the 1950s and early 1960s, was grossly lacking and not just in funds. For what the alternative therapies movement has articulated is also a growing discontent with 'professionalism' – precisely that attribute so lauded in the early days of the National Health Service. That particular image of the 'expert', the rational scientist who could diagnose through his high level of scientific knowledge and in whom one had absolute trust, has gone. Instead discontent has grown with obscurantism, and with lack of time or interest in the patient as another human being. Books like *How to Raise a Healthy Child in spite of Your Doctor*[3] show that the doctor for many people has ceased to be the kindly mediator of high science to the population. Instead, he or she is seen as a professional with vested interests, a professional who is concerned as much with his or her position in the hierarchy as with the comfort or rights of the patient, and a professional who, occasionally, covers up mistakes.

Nothing more clearly articulates the criticisms of conventional medicine than this changed perception of the doctor and the hospital. All the alternative therapists I spoke to criticized the existing system and existing relationship between doctor and patient. The doctors, they said, neglected any real human contact with their patient. They regarded human bodies as their possessions, over which they had absolute power and rights to decide the course of treatment. There was rarely any attention to an individual's feelings or emotions, even when the individual was given a devastatingly bleak prognosis. Alternative therapies, on the contrary, offered proper personal contact and engendered in the individual a sense of control over their bodies and health. Adherents to the alternatives accounted for their appeal in terms of a 'higher level of consumer consciousness' or a general criticism of inhuman and bureaucratic attitudes.

Most practitioners, however, were keen to attribute the widespread discontent with doctors not just to the failings of conventional medicine itself, but to a new consciousness of the value of involving the individual in her or his well-being and a new sense of the value of being natural. The general public, they say, are no longer happy to be treated as impersonal bodies with standard treatments. Instead they want a sensitive recognition of themselves and their needs. Thus, most of those involved in the alternative health movement interpret their widespread success as being based on the fact that they are genuinely *alternative*, in philosophies and techniques.

Of course there is a strong contingent of practitioners who will not accept this designation of 'alternative'. They prefer the term 'complementary' and are quick to stress that they accept many of the practices and approaches of conventional medicine. These groups also express the deepest ambivalence about the critique of 'professionalism'. Although they would share the criticisms of inhumanity and distance from the patient, they are not prepared to disregard the necessity for professional bodies, examinations and structures by which practitioners of alterative therapies can be called to account. Yet, even for these practitioners, there is an underlying sense that they do offer a real alternative even if their ultimate aspiration is that orthodox medicine will adopt the values of complementary medicine. What they wish is that orthodox medicine would become more like them – 'natural', 'caring' and 'integrated'.

But the attractions of alternative medicine are always in excess of these criticisms of orthodox medicine. The tidal wave that has carried alternative therapies to the forefront of people's consciousness is far broader than just a discontent with the existing medical profession. Nothing makes this clearer than the fact that the criticisms of orthodox medicine have not been translated into a more thorough *political* critique of existing health service practices. All the criticisms which I have mentioned so far could have very direct political consequences. Yet, on the whole political change has not occurred. The criticisms of orthodox medicine have not resulted in attempts to change existing services but in a turning away altogether in favour of new approaches and practices, practices where an entirely new view of the body is enshrined.

It is, for example, quite possible to see much of the inhumanity of hospitals and doctors as deriving from work structures, in particular professional hierarchies and rigid divisions between experts (consultants, etc.) and those who actually do the caring for patients. Nurses are badly paid, undervalued, and given very little real responsibility for a patient, yet they are responsible for day-to-day care. Medicine, almost more than any of the other professions, has also been infected by a machismo work ethic where the senior positions are almost all filled by men who have staked their identity on being able to work long hours without betraying any weakness or emotion. In a hierarchy like this there are just too many holes. No one directly caring for the patient is fully responsible for her or him and 'caring' itself is seen as inferior to the skills of the expert. It is a recipe for disaster.

Viewed from this perspective, there clearly is a possible politics of health which goes a lot further than questions of how much funding hospitals should have and whether the public should pay for their treatment. There could be a politics aimed at breaking down professional hierarchies, and at changing attitudes towards caring. It would be possible to imagine a politics which was concerned with making relations between patients and the medical profession more humane, and making doctors more answerable to their patients' needs. But these are not the main concerns within alternative medicine, any more than they are the concerns of those within orthodox medicine. And this is because the critique of the medical orthodoxy launched by alternative therapies is not primarily political in the sense of seeking changes in structures and organizations of existing health services.

What could be a political critique of conventional medicine is instead a critique based on a *philosophical* opposition to orthodox medicine and attitudes towards health. Criticisms of organizations, structures, hierarchies and divisions of labour have been added to something much wider, a full-scale criticism of the values of conventional attitudes towards health. The alternative health movement has given voice to a fundamental philosophical opposition to past ways of viewing health, a criticism which runs from the overdependency of the medical profession on dangerous synthetic drugs right through to a critique of 'the spiritual bankruptcy' of orthodox medicine. For many, the notion of being alternative is considerably more than just doing it differently from orthodox medicine. It is also a symbolic activity. It is a profound expression of a new consciousness which individuals have about health and the body. This involves a commitment to finding a new life style, to pursuing a new well-being, and to finding 'natural' ways of achieving this well-being. Above all it is a new consciousness of the importance of the individual in achieving health.

Alternative therapies talk of a 'new age', an age where the individual is no longer part of a system or bureaucracy but is recognized in her or his full individuality. And frequently this new attention to the individual is represented as an attention to things 'spiritual'. Sharing the views and aspirations of the alternative health movement is very often considerably more than sharing a critique of orthodox medicine. More often than not it is to share this commitment to the natural, to the involvement of the individual in well-being and to sense that the spiritual side of humankind has been badly neglected. Alternative therapists often represent themselves as giving voice to these new yearnings:

> there has been an increasing seeking on the part of many for a new sense of purpose and understanding to their lives, one which goes beyond both the purely materialistic and the dogma put forth by many established religions . . . To those involved with any kind of esoteric or human potential movement it is clear we are in the midst of a time of spiritual as well as material change

and that there is a great need for a fundamental shift to take place within the planetary consciousness.[4]

However extreme these views might appear, however redolent with a hippie mysticism distrusted even by those in the alternative therapies movement they have loud echoes inside and outside the alternative therapies movement. They give voice to something which is not self-evident. A *health* movement has become the repository of any number of aspirations about individuals achieving a new state of spiritual awareness.

Given these almost religious claims, the popularity of alternative therapies seems all the more extraordinary. This is far more than a perfectly valid critique of orthodox medicine. It is the construction of a whole edifice of beliefs on the notion of good health. And the only possible explanation for the massive increase in popularity of these ideas is that they correspond to widespread changes in the popular perception of physical and emotional states which has provided fertile ground for alternative therapies to flourish. In a sense it is right to talk of a 'new age', although I do not use the term in the same uncritical way. For, taken over all, the ideas symbolized by the alternative health movement do represent a revolution, a revolution of 'consciousness' affecting everyday attitudes to health, the body and related issues like food and sex. Many of the attitudes and philosophies behind these 'alternatives' are much more widespread than one might imagine from their designation as 'alternative' practices. Even within orthodox medicine (perhaps the most closed and sceptical of any social force) some of the principles behind alternative medicine are beginning to infiltrate. A recent survey of medical students revealed that 80 per cent of them in fact wanted to know more about alternative medicine and would contemplate referring patients to alternative practitioners. But in other more socially significant ways too we can see correspondences with the beliefs and ideas fundamental to alternative medicine.

There are profound correspondences between views of the body, health and nature in the alternative therapies movement, and in almost all popular writing on health. Wherever we look, it is hard to escape the emphasis which is currently put on the importance of life style, on the importance of the individual in illness and health and on the importance of natural approaches (to eating, to medicine, and so on). It is hard to escape a call for the involvement of the 'whole' person – body, mind, emotions and spirit – in the pursuit of well-being, even if we have not been specifically involved in any therapy. We are bombarded in the press and the media with information about how to look after our health and the importance of so doing. It is hard to avoid the implication that health has taken over from sex as the main area of personal self-determination. And it would not be far out to suggest a national obsession with good health, or natural good health, an obsession which makes us receptive to the values of the alternative health movement.

The general prevalence and acceptance of ideas which do not appear to use 'orthodox' scientific explanations of the human body cause some people to bewail. The hard-boiled 'materialists' of the 1960s who scoffed at hippie mysticism see their own systems of thought in pathetic disarray compared with the vigour of their opposites. They perceive themselves as a beleaguered minority in a land peopled with mystics, those, that is, who have not already trained as naturopaths or acupuncturists. Those who have accepted new attitudes towards the individual, health and the body view the old 'materialists' as historical relics, products of a bygone era who have failed to move on in time. It would be easy in the current welter of publications, and so on, to think that the alternative has pretty well become the mainstream. Undoubtedly the reason for this impression is that the philosophies behind these alternative practices are even more widespread than the practices themselves. Though they still term themselves alternative, and indeed are so in relation to the dominant practices, they neverthe-less express views of nature, of the person and of the relationship between the physical and the emotional which are far from alternative and fringe. Indeed, I would claim that these views are beginning to dominate popular conceptions of the relationship between body and mind.

Assertions about 'dominant ways of seeing the world' are always difficult. I can imagine a practitioner of alternative medicine reading this introduction who would be outraged at my suggestion that their way of viewing the world might be more dominant than that of orthodox medicine. The practitioner of alternative medicine will see her/himself as relatively powerless, servicing an increasingly sympathetic public but without any medical recognition or the attribution of resources that would go with that recognition. The practitioners of alternative medicine have very little actual power, a particularly galling situation when they also regard themselves either as 'complementing' orthodox medicine where it has little success or indeed sometimes as picking up the pieces of orthodox medicine's clumsy handling of its patients. So I should make it clear that in talking about a revolution in attitudes I am not talking about a change in power. Instead, I am talking about the changes which have made the public so receptive, even though orthodox medicine still does, in a very real sense, dominate and control many people's experiences of health and illness.

In short, this book is tracing a changed 'episteme' as the French philosopher Michel Foucault called it. This is a change in sets of beliefs and attitudes, where the body, health and nature have come to mean different things and imply different consequences for the individual. In the following chapters I will attempt to trace the exact elements in these changes. I will examine in detail some of the cornerstones of alternative therapies like beliefs in the 'whole person', in the importance of health foods and in the possibility of self-transformation. In particular I will attempt to unpick the meanings that cluster around some of the concepts most frequently taken for granted within the alternative health movement, concepts like well-being, nature, holism, women's intuition, personal change and the possibility of wholeness. My aim is to understand the deeper significance of the emergence of these ideas at this moment, and to ask questions about how and why health has come to dominate our consciousness.

Notes

1 'Complementary Medicine in the U.K.', Research Council for Complementary Medicine, June 1986.
2 Report on Alternative Medicines, British Medical Association, 1986.
3 Robert S. Mendelsohn, *How to Raise a Healthy Child in spite of Your Doctor*.
4 'Information about the Foundation', Foundation for Holistic Consciousness.

1 Nature –
Not 'red in tooth and claw'

'Nature' is probably the most important concept in the alternative health movement. To claim that a therapy, medicine or food is 'natural' is to validate it instantly. For the general public, therapies like homoeopathy, herbalism or reflexology automatically mean 'natural'. Indeed, names like 'Natural Health Clinic' and 'natural health movement' almost invariably signal the presence of alternative therapies. 'Alternative' and 'natural' have become interchangeable concepts even if many of the alternative practitioners don't make a particular thing of being natural. And it goes without saying that the interchangeability of these concepts works to the advantage of alternative therapies. To be natural is to be automatically different from, and better than, orthodox medicine. This sense of the virtue of being natural is by no means confined to alternative therapies. It is a widespread and prevalent feeling: if it's natural, then it must be good for us.

Yet how often do we stop to think about what 'nature' actually implies when it is used so freely in these new concerns about our health? For the meaning of the term nature is not self-evident, a transparent reflection of some objective reality of fields and animals. Nature is a term whose meanings have changed over the course of history. And very often what is meant by the term nature tells us more about the inner preoccupations of people at a particular moment, rather than any objective knowledge of nature. In the new health movement nature is a central concept in a mythology about people's relationships with one another, with animals, plants and society. The term 'nature' as it is currently used is a symbol redolent with beliefs and meanings about health, the body and the ideal state of the human being. And I hope to show that this contemporary mythology of nature embodies desires and aspirations which have definite consequences for how individuals think of their place in society.

The idea that it is virtuous to be natural permeates much of contemporary Western society. In the late twentieth century, as technological developments continue unabated, large numbers of people are obsessed with the idea of finding more 'natural' ways to live. Everywhere we look we find evidence of this quest for naturalness, for food and activities following 'natural' principles. The formula 'contains only natural ingredients with no additives, chemicals or artificial preservatives' is like an instant guarantee of health and happiness. It is emblazoned on numerous packages and tins. Even added on to highly processed food for sale in the large supermarkets, it signals more than just the *absence* of certain substances; it signals the presence of some additional virtuous quality. Everywhere we look there is evidence of an overwhelming drive to deny 'artificiality' or 'processing' and to emphasize the natural.

Advertisers, similarly, use the term natural as if it magically transferred desirable attributes to their products. With the addition of the term, the products will acquire instant therapeutic and beneficial properties. Creighton's preparations will work, we are told, because: 'Nature herself has been the model and the provider.' Foods, vitamin and mineral supplements and beauty products are all promoted as natural and beneficial because they act on the body only as nature intended. 'Be gentle on your skin as nature intended – naturally.'[1] Even advertisements for the most sophisticated technology attempt to attract to themselves the great virtues implied by the term natural. Thus Kenwood food processors are sold by using images of the machine amidst a cornucopia of fresh produce. The caption 'Kenwood, naturally' implies the inevitability, and good sense, of choosing this machine for aiding the domestic preparation of fresh, natural foods. The contradiction of emphasizing the natural to sell what is highly technological is glossed over. All around us products offer to transfer to us some of the virtues of 'natural goodness'.

In recent years 'nature' – viewed in this way – has taken on unparalleled significance. Everyone appears to be convinced of the virtues of eating naturally, of living as natural a life style as possible, of following natural principles. Most people seem to take it for granted that natural and goodness are two words that belong happily together. Most people probably don't stop to think twice about this meaning of natural. They share a 'commonsense' definition of nature as that which has not been technologically and commercially exploited or transformed. The implication is that, left alone, natural products are kind and caring, that they supply nutrients and ingredients which are beneficial to personal well-being. Certainly when we see the rows of products with names like Harvest Munch, Meadow Fresh, Wild Thyme Products, it is clear we are being sold a vision of nature as non-technological, as meadows, simple harvests, and wild herbs. And the vision is one which is meant to suggest goodness, wholesomeness and virtue.

Behind this apparently simple picture of the virtues of natural life lies a whole series of relatively new beliefs about what nature is, why it is good and beneficial, and how the human being fits into nature. Nature has not always been thought of in such benign terms. Indeed, at various points in Western history the highest aspiration has been to move as far away as possible from 'savage' nature. The concept of nature is, in fact, almost always an important one for human societies, even though it means different things to different cultures and at different epochs. Views of what nature is, and how people fit into patterns of nature, are crucial elements in a culture's self-definition and social ideologies. Invariably they provide a way for people to think about their own existence and what it implies to be human. In the eighteenth century, the main source of ideas about the state of nature were so-called primitive societies. Rousseau saw nature embodied in what he called 'the noble savage'. The noble savage was 'primitive' man in his uncivilized state; he was wild, savage, uncultured. Yet he was also 'noble', untainted by the degradations of civilized life, a magnificent innocent. Of course, these views did not represent any real understanding of so-called primitive societies or mankind in a natural state. Instead they expressed views on Western civilization. Although people in Western societies were cultured and intellectual, Rousseau saw man as having definitively fallen from grace.

Civilization had corrupted the soul of man, taking people away from their wild but strangely innocent natural selves.

These changing views of nature show that there is no such thing as 'nature' in a pure form. There are only terrains and species of plants and animals known and interpreted by various cultures at different historical moments. There are only ever 'hypotheses' about what people would be like in their natural form. And nothing could illustrate this more clearly than the contemporary obsession with the natural and nature. In certain ideologies – and the alternative health movement is crucial here – 'nature' has been laden with definite assumptions about what qualities nature has and, therefore, how these qualities would be expressed by people and animals living in a 'natural' state. Nature has come to carry a whole series of selective meanings about wholesomeness, goodness, purity and health. And as we look more closely at these meanings we will see exactly how they relate to a new mythology of good and evil, of degeneracy and renewal, which is focused on ideas of the body, health and the state of nature.

The corruptions of modern life

The implications of the claim to be 'natural' made by so many alternative therapies are rather unclear, which should prepare us for the cluster of ideological meanings surrounding the term. Precise definitions of natural therapies are rare but where they are found they fall within certain parameters. The World Federation of Healing, for instance, describes natural therapies as those which 'use only substances, methods and modalities which in trained and experienced hands are perfectly safe and therefore cannot give rise to harmful side effects'. Their list of 'natural therapies' includes homoeopathy, osteopathy, naturopathy, acupuncture, psychotherapy, healing, chiropractic, herbalism, radionics, dietetics. The most frequent implication of being natural is being the opposite of orthodox medicine. What is implied by this is that natural therapies are 'non-technological', 'non-drug based' and 'non-invasive'. We are told, for instance, that herbal remedies 'do not have the aggressive and invasive action of modern drugs. Instead they provide the necessary trace elements, vitamins, and medical substances in a harmonious whole so as to restore full health to patients without causing harmful side effects.'[2]

These definitions of natural are pretty loose; they are not based on any scientific examination of nature. Rather they assert that orthodox medicine runs counter to the laws of nature and employs destructive and militaristic techniques. But within these loose views we can detect three main criteria for naturalness; absence of technology in either production of medicines or treatment of patients, safety, and working with the 'natural forces' of the body. Nature by implication is that which is safe, gentle and has inherent properties which will benefit individuals. Natural therapies are regularly promoted as being safe, gentle, kind to the body, and working with the body; they are 'generally not as dramatic as drugs, because they are gentle and have a more subtle approach they sometimes take longer to work'.[3]

The first criterion, that of hostility to technologically based medicine seems to belong, at least in part, to the general hostility to technology and human artefact, often described as artificiality or processing. Many of the therapies emphasize their claim to naturalness precisely because nothing comes between the interaction of two human beings. Thus the manipulative therapies such as osteopathy, acupressure, rolfing, structural integration and so on stress their great advantage as treatments on the grounds that they are nothing more than the activities of one person's hands on another person's body. We are told, for example, that the Alexander technique, 'by the use of hands, guides . . . the pupil back to a position of poise'.[4] Similarly, some physiotherapy 'encompasses natural techniques based on the use of touch to treat pain, illness and disability'.[5] But even these techniques are too interventionist for some. Ortho-bionomy, for example, 'uses no force to influence the realignment of the structure but uses the natural reflex of the body and the aura to achieve results'.[6] Although these activities do not occur in nature, that is they are human and social techniques, nevertheless they are seen as natural because they do not involve technology and they guide or realign the body so that it can heal itself naturally.

Secondly, alternative therapies base their claim to naturalness on being non-drug based. When alternative therapies do use 'substances' the aim is to keep them as natural as possible. The precise distinction between orthodox medicines and natural medicines is that the latter are not 'synthetic', that is they are not artificially produced compounds. The dislike of anything synthetic in these philosophies derives from an obsessional opposition between 'natural' and 'artificial' which we will find cropping up again and again in the various strands of alternative therapies. The much-distrusted 'synthetically' produced compounds are those which involve the creation of substances which do not necessarily occur in nature in that form. The emphasis in alternative medicine is on the opposite; practitioners stress that they only use substances which occur in nature in the same form. Herbal practitioners specify their disagreement with and distrust of the conventional pharmaceutical approach because it seeks to find, isolate and synthesize an active principle, as in the production of aspirin from willow bark or digoxin from the foxglove.

These active ingredients are in the long run incompatible with good health. In plants, however, these powerful constituents are balanced and made accessible to body tissues by the numerous other constituents present. The Chinese drug *Ma Huang*, for example, yields ephradine, an alkaloid which raises blood pressure if given as an extracted drug. In the whole plant however there are six other alkaloids the main one of which actually prevents a rise in blood pressure and an increase in the heart rate. The isolated drug is dangerous but the whole plant is balanced by nature to make it a safer remedy.[7]

Not all alternative therapies have the same rigorous commitments to the 'whole' plant as herbalism. But most share this commitment to only 'natural' substances. Homoeopathy, of all the alternative medicines, is the least concerned with naturalness. One practitioner told me that homoeopathy was far less concerned with 'naturalness' than with 'safety'. The same practitioner expressed anxiety about some of the other alternative therapies. He thought that some of the substances used in herbalism were toxic however natural they might be. In inexperienced hands they could well be dangerous. And these worries are certainly not without foundation, since there are plenty of naturally occurring substances which can be lethal – rhubarb leaves and uncooked kidney beans, for example. Aromatherapy has come in for similar criticisms. Without proper instructions for use, some of the substances for sale could be dangerous; peppermint extract could cause severe burning to the stomach if taken internally in ignorance. The homoeopathic practitioner who had raised the issue of naturally occurring poisons, argued that homoeopathy was better able to guarantee safety since the quantities used of any substance were so minute as to defy harm. Even so homoeopaths regularly draw attention to the fact that all homoeopathic drugs are drawn from 'minerals', 'animal extracts' and 'nosodes' and that 'nothing is synthesized'.[8] And this is undoubtedly offered as a strength and virtue of the system.

These ideas are typical. They signal the intense belief in the virtues of using something in its original, 'natural' form, rather than something which has been extracted and combined. According to this philosophy, anything which seeks to isolate elements of what grows and occurs naturally will destroy the capacity of the plant and nature to do good. Indeed, by interfering, the components of plants and minerals are converted into something with the capacity to do harm – usually presented as 'chemicals'. 'Chemical' is one of those terms within the alternative health movement which has become loaded with negative implications. Anything chemical must be bad. It implies synthesizing, processing, and conjures up visions of research laboratories staffed by profit-hungry scientists in white coats. 'Chemical' has been set up as a polar opposite of 'natural'. Yet it is in fact almost impossible to draw hard and fast lines between chemical and natural substances. Many chemicals are 'naturally' occurring; many chemicals are derived from 'natural' substances. The opposition within the alternative health movement is really an opposition between something 'original' and something transformed by human activity.

We are clearly faced with an opposition which goes way beyond an actual distinction. This is an opposition which insists on the superiority of elements in an original, 'whole' form, over elements which have been touched by people. This opposition between the natural and the artificial is fundamental to the alternative health movement but it is rather a precarious opposition. After all, any activity of mankind, even scientific and technological pursuits, could be said to be 'natural' activities of mankind. It is possible to argue that people have a 'natural' instinct to live in societies and that any complex social and industrial developments that take place, therefore, are just an expression of humanity's natural talents. To place science, industry and technology in consistent opposition to nature is to make nature an entirely imaginary place, without any human society. Nature in this fantasy is where you can find elements and substances untouched by human activity, and experience an original wholeness. It is a fantasy which has its roots in a hostility to machinery born in the rapid social changes of the Industrial Revolution.

Nature, in these views, is only ever dangerous or harmful after humans have interfered, as in the consequences of radiation or the use of artificial fertilizers and pesticides in farming. Only then does nature acquire the capacity to do harm to the individual. Otherwise, what occurs in uninterrupted nature is always good. Human operations which involve any technology are viewed with suspicion. Indeed, traditional 'scientific' and technological activity is seen as hostile and militaristic, producing substances which are aggressive and invasive, working against rather than for the body. In opposition, that which is natural is necessarily seen as being gentle, kind, positive, and always beneficial. This idea of the gentleness and safety of nature is one that currently extends way beyond alternative medicine. Again advertisers reveal an acute grasp of general philosophical trends; they stress a product's naturalness because that is supposed to imply gentleness and kindness. Invariably we encounter comments of the kind that 'natural' products only behave as nature herself would, that is, gently and in co-operation with the body. No one seems to notice the contradiction in the idea of 'natural products'. Simultaneously it implies that the product is manufactured but natural, two mutually contradictory states in these new views of nature.

What is at work here are a number of significant oppositions, for example, artificial versus natural, technological versus organic, synthesized versus the whole or original form. The implied criticism of the 'unnatural' is not presented as a political criticism of the way in which technology and agriculture have developed in the West. Instead the criticism is channelled into a philosophical opposition between modern society and nature, implying an opposition between that which is irretrievably harmful and that which is totally beneficial. Harm is very firmly on the side of what mankind does. Humans and their technology are the forces which cause life to degenerate, a position clearly embodied in this advertisement for the International Institute of Symbiotic Studies.

> We are faced with severe microbial imbalances which not only affect human health but which permeate all forms of life: soil, water, plants and animals. With the rapidly increasing degeneration in the quality of life the main concern of the institute is to promote the research and education of ecological healing methods which genuinely reverse this downward spiral of degeneration.[9]

Nature in 'original' form is always beneficial, never degenerative or corrupting.

The emphasis placed on natural practices, medicines and products is in part expressing a criticism of the modern and the technological. But it goes further than that. It is also recirculating a religious opposition, between the degenerate or corrupt and the regenerative and healthy, in which mankind has destroyed an original wholeness. Technology, artefact, science, machinery are all seen as the forces which have caused not only fragmentation but illness and degeneration. In order to better understand how this opposition has been integrated into a critique of modern society, we need to understand more precisely what is implied by the term natural. What evidence do the adherents to 'natural therapies' have for their assertion that nature is beneficial and will look after the body, and that nature in its 'original' form is safer and kinder than anything which people can produce?

Gentle nature

The idea that nature is beneficial is based largely on a set of beliefs about the 'properties' of nature, in particular on a hypothesis about the properties of the natural (original) body. In virtually all the alternative therapies there is a strong and fundamental belief in the body's 'natural' will towards health, in its inherent capacity to be well and to return to health given the proper conditions. All the therapies I have examined claim that they do not offer a magic 'cure', as conventional medicine promises. Instead, they are activities, designed to release the natural healing processes of the body. Relaxation is, for example, 'nature's healing gift'; T'ai Chi is 'the natural way to peace and harmony'; and naturopathy, expressing views common to the whole movement, speaks of the body as self-healing. 'The healing of wounds and the repair of broken bones are universally recognized as manifestations of this self-restorative power of the body. Few people realize however that acute conditions such as colds, fevers, etc. are in most cases indications that the healing force is applying itself to the task of removing obstructions to normal functioning of organ or tissue.'[10]

Indeed the whole function of alternative therapies is often presented as simply helping the body restore itself, attacked as it has been by the stresses and strains of modern life. 'Alternative therapies seek to work *with* the body, and not against it, enhancing its powerful instinct to heal itself.'[11] Health is a state of nature, a gift freely given but easily lost. 'Health is the normal, natural state of the human being and it is maintained quite without conscious control by that wonderful, normalizing, building, healing "intelligence" which is sometimes called "nature" or "vital force". It is that which heals wounds, repairs broken bones, builds blood, tissue and muscles and eliminates waste matter. It is always working to a pre-ordained plan of perfection and normality.'[12]

The idea of the body as self-healing has become a linchpin for claims about the attributes of nature. That viruses appear to occur in nature is passed over in silence. So too is the inevitable end of life. Instead, from the fact that the body will often heal, renew itself and fight off illness, a whole series of assumptions have been made about nature. If the body can heal like this, then nature is about renewal. If the body renews, then nature must have vital forces, or essential energies, energies which run through human, animal and plant bodies, energies which work for our benefit. These energies, so long as they are balanced and properly attended to (unblocked), constitute the natural health and vitality of the individual. It is these energies which provide the body with its capacity to renew and return to health. Almost all the therapies I have looked at account for their successes as having simply unblocked or re-balanced the energies, thus allowing the body to return to health. In some therapies there is a belief that 'natural' medicine itself embodies these energies as in the claim of aromatherapy that 'pure essential oils have been called the "life force of plants" as they contain the healing properties of that plant in a whole and concentrated form'.[13]

'Energy' is assumed to be the force behind nature's vigorous renewal. It is the common factor between humans and 'natural' substances. Typically, a T'ai Chi expert described the essence of humanity as being energy. 'The key to the advanced work of T'ai Chi is understanding energy, exploring its different types and forms. Energy is the essence of the person, that which makes them a human being.'[14] What is beneficial to the human is the transfer of the vital, curative energies of the plants and natural substances which have been tampered with by human activities. And it is in plants, herbs, flowers and vegetables where this life force and the true experience of natural energy resides.

> It is a welcome relief to watch the credibility the women (in cultures not subject to the pressure of advertising) give these plants when our Western boffins hastily scuttle over accumulated findings of the past, tested through centuries of use with a thoroughness no laboratory programme could now afford. Speed is the essence of today. Meanwhile acres of wild flowers grow and bloom and die natural deaths, their offers refused, their powers to heal ignored.[15]

The notion of life forces and vital energies and how they heal is highly selective. Only certain substances instantly convey these essential energies. No one suggests eating a freshly killed young rabbit on the grounds that its life forces would greatly benefit the consumer. Plants and plants alone embody these mysterious attributes of nature. Gone is any talk of 'nature, red in tooth and claw'. Nature is no longer the terrain, as in Tennyson's day, where the strong appeared to destroy the weak and where survival through competition was a sign of strength and health. In these current views there is little place for the idea of the struggle within and between species for survival. 'Nature' as a concept now excludes violence and aggression. We have moved an enormous distance from Darwin whose ideas dominated philosophical views of nature for a long while. In his ideas, competition and aggression were absolutely crucial. The environment was conceived as basically hostile in that resources were limited. Not only did species struggle between themselves for access to limited resources but aggression was also at the basis of evolution within the species. According to Darwin, male sexual display and the selection of the strongest, most flamboyant male exponent of the species by a female, was the way in which a species developed the particular attributes by which it survived in its niche.

If pushed, exponents of contemporary views of nature would probably accept evolutionary arguments, but in a highly modified form. Contemporary views of nature imply neither dynamic evolution nor a struggle for survival. On the contrary they concentrate on the interrelation between plants and species. The emphasis is on how the species relate to each other in harmony to the benefit of one another. Nature is seen as having evolved in order to benefit the neighbours in a chain of life. This view of nature as ecologically interdependent is by no means confined to the alternative health movement, although as we shall see the health movement has given this view its own special inflection. We can see evidence of this widespread change in the understanding of the relationship between species and man in general changes in attitudes towards nature.

One example which makes clear the shifts in views of nature, is zoos. In the middle of the last century when the zoological garden first became popular, nature and her wonders were viewed in very different ways from now. Even the name zoological garden reveals the difference. Like the great botanical gardens with their displays of flowers and plants from all over the world, zoos aimed at doing the same for the animal kingdom. Western society was to be given the chance to marvel at the wonders of the world, the endless variety of species, of variations between the species and within the species. Cramped cages were erected side by side with little regard for the animals' well-being. The point was to display the animals well for the visitors. And what these displays made possible was Knowledge, human knowledge, the classification of all species, knowledge of the entire world and all her products and the processes by which she had evolved. The early zoo was pre-eminently encyclopaedic, a place where the visitor could know the entire world and wonder at its endless variety. In so far as anything was implied about the place of the human within nature, it was a relationship of difference. Humanity was either radically different from the animals or infinitely superior, the end product of the evolutionary process.

What could be further from the stated ideologies of contemporary zoos? In new zoos it is not always easy to see the animals. The emphasis is ostensibly not on the display of the animals to the visitors but on the animals' original and natural environments. There are invariably long notices explaining what the various physical features of the animals are and how they evolved. The aim is to demonstrate the processes of adaptation of animals to their environment. Nature in these displays is infinitely ingenious; each and every feature of the animal and its behaviour has a purpose. And zoos claim to teach us how to respect those purposes. Yet we are constantly reminded of the damage which humans can do to the delicate and complex balance of nature. Those zoos left with their original bleak and bare pens hastily convert or guiltily justify their inability to change by reference to ecological arguments. Zoos, we are told, can help maintain threatened species. Zoos can be places where people repay nature. Although, for the animals, the experience is probably much as it always was, in this current approach is to be found the ideal of equality and harmony between animals and human beings. We are all species together but people have abused their cultural advantages. Increasingly, zoos carry a message of guilt. Humans should be self-abasing in the face of the marvellous interdependence and efficiency of nature. And humans should feel especially remorseful for the harm done to the animal world.

These contemporary attitudes towards zoos share many elements of the view of nature in alternative therapies. 'Nature' is infinitely superior to modern society. The advance of technology has only brought harm and our dominant reaction to mankind's achievements should be one of guilt. Yet there are added elements in the philosophies behind alternative therapies. In addition to the oppositions between technology as bad or harmful, and nature as gentle but energetic, there is a further opposition between disorder or fragmentation and order or harmony. If we cast our minds back to the earlier quotation about herbalism where the importance of using the 'whole plant' was discussed, we can begin to grasp the meanings of this further opposition. For within alternative therapies, the general 'ecological' consciousness of the interdependence of the species has been transformed into a much more definite hypothesis about the properties of nature and their purpose.

Within alternative therapies there is often a suggestion of a natural 'holism' or interdependence between elements which amounts almost to a divine purpose. Nature's basic intentions are expressed in the perfect balance of elements within nature which makes it so kind and beneficial towards humanity, and especially to health. In the earlier quotation about herbalism, it is clear that only the whole plant, as it originally grew, will contain the substance beneficial for health. In herbal medicine the plant is balanced, each component part of the plant is working in harmony with other parts and for a purpose.

> When the chemist or the doctor uses herbal extracts in prescriptions they are either mixed with a chemical product, or the active principle is extracted from the plant and used in isolation from the other parts regarded as having no value. In either case, the herbalist claims that such treatment is not as effective as when the complete plant is used.[16]

This reference to the perfect balance between elements of a plant or between various plants in herbalism is not an isolated one. The attitude towards synthetic products described earlier was a similar hostility to the destruction of an original wholeness. And this sense of nature as being balanced and having a natural 'holism' is where we begin to see quite clearly the new mythologizing of the concept of nature.

Wholeness, balance and harmony

Ideas about natural balances and proper relations between humans and nature are not confined to alternative therapies; they are a variant of a much more general 'ecological' consciousness with its strong commitment to the idea of natural life cycles and relations which have been seriously disrupted by human activities. But in alternative therapies these ideas take a particular form; ideas of balance and harmony in nature and of a proper relation between people and nature are fundamental to definitions of what nature *is*. And the key to this definition is Health. Health is a natural state, yet health can only be achieved by exploring a sense of wholeness, balance and harmony within ourselves. Therefore, so the arugment runs, nature must itself express the values of wholeness, harmony and balance. So crucial are these assumptions that many practitioners give as their definition of a natural therapy that which helps individuals find this proper balance, either by adjusting the posture of the body, or by changing diet, life style or outlook, or by taking medicine which will correct the imbalances which have arisen in the body.

Crucial in this hypothesis about nature is a belief in, or should we call it a fantasy of, an original state of the body, with 'natural' impulses. In alternative therapies, there are often recommendations for a return to a more natural life style. This is presented as being in harmony with patterns and cycles of nature.

> The advice I would give to any young man going into modern sedentary occupations in commerce and industry is first to realise that to combine such a life with a healthy one is a contradiction in terms. Healthy people rise at dawn, work physically all day in the open and go to bed pleasantly exhausted at sundown. They live on a diet which is unadulterated, living and fresh and can maintain full health without the aid of flesh foods.[17]

This vision of natural living is hopelessly romantic and deluded; it is a fantasy of a wholesome 'peasant' past where working in the fields, eating only fresh vegetables, produced the healthy man. The wickedly funny representations of peasant life in Monty Python's *Holy Grail*, and *Jabberwocky*, are probably closer to the constant struggle against hunger, lack of sanitation and disease which actually accompanied such a life style.

Of course, not all the views of a natural life style are quite as hopelessly romantic as the one quoted. But the idea of a healthy and natural life is common, even if it is only ever a concept and not something which can be realistically achieved amidst the stresses and strains of modern life. In this context natural therapies are represented as the necessary compensations; they can help us find within the individual body the forces of nature. If modern life has deprived us of original health, alternative therapies can unlock our natural potential for health. The body in this ideology has an instinct for health and craves a proper relation to nature. Once freed from the corruptions and distortions of modern life and modern life and technological society, the tendency of the body to heal and renew itself is taken as evidence of a fundamental, natural inclination.

There is a strong sense that the body in its original form, or when restored to its original good health, will know instinctively what is right and healthy for it. It is as if the body has become the site of all innocence, which for a while was attributed by religions to the soul of the child. Now it is the body which innocently aspires towards all that is good and wholesome, the body which deeply aspires towards a proper relation with nature.

> The body is self-adjusting. Left to itself, everyone would tend towards healthiness and balance with nature. A central theme of all natural therapies is the notion of natural life cycles and their interconnections . . . The body and the world are self-adjusting and we must not interfere. There is a wonderful balance in nature – a balance which is repeated through the universe, from the structure of the atom to the position of the earth in the solar system.[18]

'Natural therapists' are keen to demonstrate this wholesome and innocent relation of the body to nature by arguing that the new-born baby instinctively knows what is good and healthy for it. Indeed breast milk is taken as further evidence of the body's natural wholesomeness. Produced by the mother's body, and sought by the new-born child, it can be construed as the ultimate symbol of an original health and purity. For the natural health movement the new-born child embodies the gift of health, a vital force which will seek to assert itself even against overwhelming odds. It is even claimed that the child has a natural instinct to eat healthily. Research is frequently quoted in which young children who had never eaten 'junk food' were allowed to select their own meals (from a number of 'healthy' alternatives). Over a number of days, although their choices seemed highly erratic, it emerged that the children had in fact eaten a highly nutritious and well-balanced combination of foods.

The new-born child here is a metaphor for the natural state of the body. It is only society which pollutes and corrupts natural taste away from what is good for it and sets the body on a consequent downward spiral of ill health, embodied in the dreaded junk foods. Obviously there is much to be said in favour of arguments which see 'taste' as socially conditioned. The way in which food preferences vary so much between cultures is enough to confirm this. But these theories completely overlook the other factors which might also influence why people choose to do or eat something which might not be conducive to good health. One anthropologist has suggested there may be a third way of regarding children's love of sweets which has nothing to do with whether or not they have a naturally sweet tooth or have been conditioned and become addicted to sugar.[19] She suggests instead that the *meanings* surrounding sweets make them highly attractive to children. In particular sweets are different from adult food and meals. She points out how sweets are invariably bought in paper bags or in highly coloured, elaborate packages. They are almost never eaten at table with a meal. Often they come in bizarre colours and shapes – worms, hats, monsters, fingers and feet in luminous green or bright orange and purple. In short they are the precise opposite of the normal meal. Sweets have nothing to do with hunger and its satisfaction or the values of nutrition. They are about inverting those values.

In this anthropological account, enjoying sweets is as much about resistance to, and freedom from, the restraints which adults place around food – that is the restraints of manners, the rituals of meals and the values of conventional taste and nutrition. But those who view the body as having a natural knowledge of what is and what is not good for it have little or no place for such a symbolic use of food. Indeed in these accounts there is little space for understanding *any* 'unhealthy' activity – be it eating, how we choose to sit, or how we behave – as anything other than a distortion of the natural or proper way foisted on us by a society which has got wildly out of touch with nature. Thus deviations from a so-called healthy way of doing things are never interpreted as real choices, having symbolic significance for the individual in question. They are always seen as the learned and conditioned responses of unfortunates cut off from a close and automatic relation with the body. To understand and be in tune with the body is given a far more significant place than anything that children might be doing symbolically with a passion for sticky, tooth-rotting sweets.

Those who believe in the body's instinct for wholesome good

health, also believe that it is only the technological and commercial exploitation of nature which has led us away from this instinctive knowledge. One of the highest goals of alternative therapies is to put the individual back in touch with these lost instincts – to re-find the true posture of the body, to rediscover natural healthy instincts of eating, or to free the body to express its own impetus towards good health. Again and again we encounter in exponents of natural health, the importance of respecting and freeing the instinctive knowledge which the body has for natural cycles, rhythms and healthiness. Indeed, some of the the therapies like bio-dynamics and bio-energetics are based exclusively on finding out about, understanding and co-operating with our natural body rhythms, whether they are digestive or sexual or some other kind of rhythm.

Once again, 'instinct', that most elastic of all concepts, is back on the agenda. And this current use of the term instinct differs little from all previous appeals to the concept, except that the details of what the instinct is are different. Whenever appeals are made to the concept of 'instinct', what is happening is that a hypothesis about the body in its original state is being used to promote the values of a particular culture or group. As with past discussions of women's 'maternal' instincts or men's 'promiscuous' instincts the hope is to provide some source, origin or justification for the values currently upheld by a particular society. Invariably the hypothesis about what the original body is or does tells us far more about the preoccupations of the society than it really does about a state of nature. As with every other previous passion for the idea of instinct, this particular version is far from a 'scientfic' study of what the body is, what it needs and what it can do.

Although many of the therapies have a pseudo-scientific edifice, when it comes to describing this natural state of the body they soon slide into a language of mysticism. The body is used as a source of ideas about 'wholeness', 'balance' and 'harmony', involving both the body and the mind. At the heart of these definitions of the natural state of humanity is a tautology. Nature is deduced from the hypothesis of the instinct of the body for health. But health is only found by discovering an inner balance and harmony. A naturally healthy body is supposed to know naturally how to be healthy. But this 'natural' knowledge has to be discovered by bringing oneself into harmony and balance, the very qualities which are supposed to be embodied by nature. A natural therapy is that which stimulates the body's natural tendency towards health; that natural tendency can only be released when the body is balanced and aligned with nature.

> Our practitioners believe that the human being must always be considered and treated as a whole, that is, that the mind, emotions and each function of the body are interdependent and should be in proper balance with each other. They also believe that this 'whole' has, as an integral part of it, a natural healing force which sustains growth and life in all living things.[20]

The exact implications of this idea of balance will be explored in later chapters. Here it is important to realize that this understanding of nature is derived from introspection. In this movement there has been a massive slide. Nature has been put under threat and has been attacked. Where she does survive she provides gentle, safe and healing energies. But nature is not to be found by going out into the wilds or by avoiding human contact, or by a relationship with the countryside or scenery. It isn't even always a question of defending those aspects of nature which are still threatened by the encroachments of technical activities. To find nature in these accounts is frequently to find something internal and mystical, something which is already there but has been lost. Nature is that healing force which is released when a proper balance can be found in the 'whole' person. In this respect, the idea of nature in the alternative health movement is significantly different from ideas of nature in ecological movements and politics. There is no requirement here for external action to preserve some hypothesized proper relationship between mankind and the environment. Instead nature can be found by attending to the inner being.

This is not to say that individuals involved in the alternative health movement are never involved in ecological politics or politics in general. For many individuals, these ideas have radical political consequences. After all, individual solutions are always limited when the individual can barely sustain access to unpolluted foods and certainly cannot control pollution in the environment. But there is no *necessity* for this. In these philosophies, a proper relationship with nature only requires an inner-directedness. And very often this inner-directedness dominates the response to external political questions: 'We cannot wait until our government has passed laws against water pollution . . . The onus, therefore, falls on the individual to solve the problem within his own home.'[21] Attitudes towards nuclear accidents and problems of radiation exemplify this inner-directedness. Although most people in the alternative health movement would undoubtedly align themselves with anti-nuclear politics, there is also an equally compelling tendency which offers 'individual' solutions to radiation. Health magazines following the Chernobyl disaster were full of articles on changes which could be made in life style and diet to minimize the effects of radiation. Obviously there's nothing wrong with people protecting themselves against the consequences of such serious accidents. But it is significant that more political and social discussions about policies around nuclear power were absent.

Equally significant is the fact that the harmonious relationship to nature is very often represented as something only to be achieved by mental as well as physical adjustments. Here meditation and relaxation techniques have become central. They are seen as the methods which allow the mind to develop the stillness which Western society denies.

> Meditation, for instance, promotes the idea of harmony within mind and body. The notion of balance is important because the West has become so active and materialistic that it has forgotten how to use that part of the brain (the left side) that is responsible for creativity, intuition and rest. Our environment has become unbalanced and hence people's desire to find stillness through meditation.[22]

At stake here is an idea that meditation can help a person become 'whole', to develop those aspects of the self which Western society has suppressed, in short to develop a naturally balanced attitude: 'The aim of meditation is based on the natural inclination of the mind to see things in their wholeness.'[23]

There is a consistent theme in these ideas that the 'still' or relaxed mind will put the individual in touch with 'natural' truth, such as the inherent wholeness in all things and the natural balance of the universe. When the mind can be explored and properly aligned, nature will be discovered. More often than not these individualistic ideas are accompanied by the language of conservatism. If nature is health, and health is wholeness, balance and harmony, then illness is represented as 'disorder', 'anarchy' and 'chaos'. Although the radicalism of vegetarianism and eco-politics does enmesh at certain points with the alternative health movement, it is much more common for a 'balanced relation to nature' to mean internal harmony and balance between the various parts of the self. And this position lends itself very readily to a conservative view of the world, where lack of acceptance and agitation are seen as the product of a non-harmonious person. As one reflexologist put it, 'As in the body, so in the state, there should be a proper balance of power, order, love and wisdom.'

Nature and tradition

Nature, in short, is not something to be known about by empirical observation, by study or science. Nature is neither scenery nor wildlife. The essence of nature, although present in all things, can be known by looking inwards, and by adjusting your existing ways in the outside world. Nature, if it cannot be known by study and classification, can be known by universal truths. And it is no coincidence that when you come to look closely, you find that the concept of nature frequently merges to the point of indistinguishability with ideas of 'the old' or 'the traditional'. Often the much-boasted naturalness of natural therapies is not so much that they occur in nature, but that they are ancient and traditional methods. Again what is at work here is a tautology. Something can be claimed as natural if it is safe, since safety is a property of nature. And safety is thought to be demonstrated if techniques and food have been used for hundreds of years.

In fact many of the alternative therapies acquire the connotations of natural simply by virtue of being ancient or traditional approaches to the body and medicine. The ancient is synonymous with the good and beneficial. 'Ma Huang', for instance, 'is one of the oldest and most famous herbs employed by Chinese herbal medicine,'[24] whereas 'The native Americans of the South West ate Blue Corn long before the yellow corn we are familiar with.'[25] Then there's a food like *mochi*, whose authenticity and healthiness is verified by the fact that it is still the food of the most traditional

Japanese families. 'Late in December in traditional villages, one can still hear the rhythmic pounding of sweet rice as families prepare mochi for the New Year's meal.'[26] The more a food was known about by primitive peoples or the more ancient or traditional a food process can be demonstrated to be, the greater its merits.

This slide between ancient and natural or healthy is by no means confined to food. Natural therapies are frequently extolled mainly on the basis of being ancient therapies. One advertisement attempts to lure people to T'ai Chi with the temptation, 'Discover how this Twelfth Century Exercise can Improve Your Health and Stimulate Meditation'. 'The East' has a privileged position in these philosophies; practices from the East carry the connotations of ancient truths, based on a 'true' understanding of nature, and sometimes linked with religions. Thus any oriental therapy carries this automatic advantage. Based on systems long used in China, India and the Far East, they carry the implication of ancient and traditional wisdoms which have a much closer relation to the body and natural instincts than anything produced in the West. Acupuncture, acupressure, and reflexology all partake in views of the body based on the 'philosophies' of oriental quasi-religions. The less well-recognized and accepted alternative therapies are especially prone to selling themselves by claims for connections with ancient truths. Reiki, for instance, 'is an ancient science which comes to us from ancient India and Tibet. Like almost all of these universal, vibratory sciences, the history of their origins lies buried deep within the spirals of our past.'[27]

For those therapies which do not come from the 'ancient' East, there is a slightly different version of the attempt to claim a heritage. Some are keen to demonstrate how their ideas do in fact link up with ancient religions and philosophies. With others there is a push to establish the therapy as deriving from a founding master, usually in the previous century. These founding figures then acquire the same sort of status as the guru of oriental religions, the status of one who understands and interprets natural truths. Rudolph Steiner for instance is represented as a person who, although founding a relatively new approach to movement and medicine, translated more ancient understandings into a contemporary context. The consistent presence of an 'originator' or the historical origins of most alternative therapies might at first appear completely straightforward. After all, most ideas do have one or two principal exponents who make certain ideas accessible to the public for the first time. Nevertheless, 'origins' and history have a great deal more significance in many of these philosophies than is strictly speaking necessary. I can think of no 'alternative' therapy which sells itself on the basis of being absolutely brand new. On the contrary, longevity, either in the form of an ancient derivation or of a past guru seems crucial to the meanings with which alternative therapy surrounds itself. To be natural cannot be to belong to the modern. To be natural is to belong to the old, the ancient, the established and the traditional.

There is a parallel tendency to that which equates ancient philosophies of the East with a closeness to nature. Any evidence that certain practices and substances are used by people from underdeveloped, non-technological societies provides an instant guarantee of the naturalness, and beneficial action, of certain substances. 'I have spent up to three months a year visiting cultures and societies that are not subject to the pressures of advertising. In areas as far afield as Africa, China, India and the Middle East, I have watched women cleanse, polish and protect their skin and hair using ingredients their mothers and grandmothers and ancestors have used and which they know work.'[28] It would be perfectly possible to put an entirely charitable interpretation on these views. After all, what they represent is a disgust with our own materialistic and consumerist society with its disregard for the environment and its excessive reliance on technologically created substances in the treatment of health.

However, there's a less charitable interpretation which could be put on this belief in some societies being closer to nature. It is what the anthropologists would call profoundly ethnocentric. In other words, it makes huge assumptions about other cultures, based on a limited understanding of them, and from the standpoint of the 'advanced' state of our own culture. The fundamental assumption is both that ancient eastern societies, and contemporary non-Western societies are somehow closer to nature than our own. It may well be empirically the case that these societies do not have the Western level of technological development. But this does not necessarily mean that those cultures were or are closer to nature. Nineteenth-century philosophers and anthropologists were taken to task at the beginning of this century for making just such assumptions. Many of these early anthropologists had believed that cultures which were not technologically advanced were therefore primitive, lacking in cultural complexity or civilization and therefore close to the state of natural man. It was only when more progressive writers challenged them that they had to abandon their ideas. People without advanced technology or without civil and political systems such as our own were not primitive. Far from it, they often had highly complex cultural, political and religious structures which had been overlooked by the early anthropologists. And religious beliefs and practices were very often found to be precisely about marking *difference* from nature rather than celebrating a similarity. To designate a culture as primitive and close to nature increasingly became the hallmark of unintelligent and racist intentions.

Of course the philosophical drive behind the current equation of ancient or non-technological societies with nature appears to be entirely different from that of the early anthropologists. In Victorian England the equation between non-technological cultures and nature was an equation which worked against those societies. They were thought to be backward, underdeveloped, uncivilized, in comparison with the achievements of Western industrial society. To be closer to nature was to be several rungs down on the evolutionary ladder. Most alternative therapists would be horrified by such an equation. Their comparison is meant to work entirely to the detriment of our own culture. Devoid of evolutionary assumptions, they simply imply that non-technological societies are without the distortions and corruptions of our own society. These other societies are better; they can see and understand nature better. They have more respect for nature. But the fact is that this is merely a reversal of the same racist assumptions. What is good and what is bad has been reversed. There is, nevertheless, a massive ideological and mythical assumption about 'the East' and about 'primitive' societies. In the same way that these societies might in the past have been imbued with mysterious sexual knowledges and attributes, they are now imbued with natural knowledges about the body and health. The point is that they are still 'the other' for our own culture, the repositories for all kinds of fantasies and projections which have little or nothing to do with how those people live or lived.

Conclusions

'Nature' then is a particularly loaded concept in alternative approaches to health. Nature is no longer scenery, the countryside or wildlife, and understanding nature certainly has nothing to do with studying and classifying those items taken to be representative of 'nature'. Nature is vital forces and energies running through all things, vital forces which lie behind the process of renewal or recovery. The main source of knowledge of these forces is the individual body. These forces of nature are beneficial and healing. Indeed, nature is health. Nature is no longer something 'external' and discoverable. Instead nature is something innate, to be found through a journey inwards, implying a relation of mind, body and outside. We can find this natural force by a process of readjustment to a proper balance and harmony with nature lost or alienated by our own modern culture. The potential inwardness of this philosophy is seen clearly in the equation of ancient philosophies or the secrets of founding fathers with an understanding of nature. 'Nature' is often explicitly philosophical rather than scientific.

This philosophy of nature is essentially static, not evolutionary. It is about discovering 'original' forms rather than any concern with the possibility of adaptation to the environment. In these approaches there is no place for the possibility that humans and animals might adapt to the things which technology throws at it. Because nature in these views is not adaptive, it is vulnerable, liable to defeat at the hands of people who are grossly at fault for their disregard of the principles of nature and natural living. And the punishment that society will carry for this disregard is illness and the inability to control chronic diseases. At the heart of these ideas of nature are a number of religious dualities, oppositions between good and evil, wholeness versus fragmentation, balance versus disharmony. Natural health has come to stand for all virtuous attributes whereas modern society and the activities of man have come to acquire all the meanings of corruption, degeneracy and decay.

This highly individualistic notion of nature is sustained by a number of different beliefs about the importance of health, about the properties of the individual body, about the relationship between mind and body, and about how to pursue a natural life style. These new beliefs amount to a new mythology of the body, health and nature. Moreover this new mythology has important consequences for how the individual will feel about her or his health, and the degree of responsibility each individual feels they must take. In the following chapters I will be exploring the various components in this new mythology. I will be asking why these beliefs have emerged at the current time, and how individuals are attracted to and captivated by these beliefs. I turn first to the whole question of why and how health has become such an important concern to so many people.

Notes

1 Advertisement for Fleur Aromatherapy.
2 Council for Complimentary and Alternative Medicine information brochure.
3 'A–Z of Alternative Health', presented with *She* magazine, 1986.
4 Information sheet for the Hale Clinic, London.
5 ibid.
6 Information sheet for Ortho-bionomy.
7 'Medical Herbalism', Council for Complimentary and Alternative Medicine brochure.
8 Interview with homoeopath.
9 Advertisement for the International Institute of Symbiotic Studies.
10 Manifesto of the British Naturopathic and Osteopathic Association, 1987–8.
11 Janet Pleshette, *Cures That Work*.
12 Tom Moule, *Nature Cure*.
13 Advertisement for Fleur Aromatherapy.
14 Interview with T'ai Chi practitioner.
15 'Natural Health', *Here's Health* magazine, Nov. 1987.
16 'Medical Herbalism', op. cit.
17 Dr Ronald Livingstone, *Healthy Living in a Polluted World*.
18 Interview with homoeopath.

19 Anne Murcott, 'You Are What You Eat: Anthropological Factors Influencing Food Choice', in Christopher Ritson et al. (eds), *The Food Consumer*.

20 Information brochure for the Nature Cure Clinic.

21 Advertisement for Purolux water purifiers.

22 Interview with Secretary, The School of Meditation, London.

23 ibid.

24 Ma Huang advertisement in *East/West* magazine, Jan. 1987.

25 Blue Corn advertisement, ibid.

26 Mochi advertisement, ibid.

27 Information brochure on Reiki-Radiance Technique.

28 *Here's Health* magazine, op. cit.

2 In Perfect Health – New Beliefs about the Body

In the late nineteenth century, Flaubert rewrote the legend of St Julian Hospitator in one of his short stories. St Julian was reputed to have helped a leper who wanted to cross the river. Instead of avoiding and ostracizing the leper, St Julian took the leper in his arms, his lips touching the diseased face. Julian was beatified for the example he set for all Christians; it was considered virtuous to accept all people in spite of disease and illness. Disease was part of the corruption of mortal life. The greatest symbol of Christian love would be someone who could reach out to the perfectible human soul encased in illness or death in their most disgusting forms. When Flaubert wrote this story, these values probably still held true. But what could be further from the views of illness and disease implicit in new concerns with good health? Contemporary messages about health and well-being insist not only that we do not have to accept disease but also that we cannot separate the soul from the body. No disease, the message runs, is beyond our control. We do not have to embrace illness.

Virtue is still an issue connected with disease but the virtue is not in the ability of humanity to accept illness, deformity and disease, but in the ability of the individual to fight them off. If 'natural health' is thought to be innate in each of us, rather than something acquirable from the outside by the use of medicines then, logically, it follows that the individual becomes responsible for his or her own health. If natural health is locked within us, waiting to be released, then it lies within the individual power to achieve health. It is clear that fairly massive changes have taken place in our views of the body and health. The corporeal body is no longer something which holds us back on our quest for perfectibility. Instead it has become the place where this perfectibility can be found. Yet, no less than with earlier views of the necessity to win salvation of the soul, now there is a sense of the necessity for the individual to work at, and win, the rewards locked in the human body.

True well-being or the possibility of perfectibility

The last few years have been witness to a radical change in what is meant by health, illness and disease. Everywhere we look the message is clear, feeling all right actually *isn't* all right. 'Feeling okay may seem enough. Indeed when you consider what some poor souls suffer, it may seem more than enough. But the truth is you could feel far better.'[1] There is a whole world of difference, we are told, between feeling all right and feeling totally healthy. And it is this concept of total health or well-being which has begun to insert itself as a positive aim, a clear concept and goal. 'We seem to know, somewhere inside us, that there is a perfect state of well-being that all our efforts are aiming towards.'[2]

Total health or true well-being are concepts which are currently extremely widespread. Indeed it is almost impossible to avoid being bombarded with messages designed to stir us to pursue these new ideals. Information about the prevention of ill health assaults us in doctors' waiting rooms, in colour supplements and in magazines. There are series on television about 'well-being' tackling major areas where we can improve our own health. We are exhorted to pursue overall fitness by changing our life styles. Even the former Junior Health Minister, Edwina Currie, told us that with attention to what we eat and how we live, we can have better health, and ward off illness. While it is doubtless the case that many of us in the affluent West have neglected our health, the current preoccupation with positive health goes far beyond any previous sense of what we might achieve individually in relation to our health. Now we can not only avoid illness, we can aim at a higher condition with a series of associated philosophical syndromes. 'Health is more than lack of disease. Health is to do with feeling good. It rests on harmony of body, soul, mind and emotion, and satisfactory relationships with other people and society as a whole.'[3]

The days appear to be definitively over when people either regarded their ailments, or minor bodily imperfections, as permanent, if unpleasant, companions. Gone too are the days of thinking of disease as misfortune, and absence of disease as good luck.

Many people have grown up with the idea that nearly all illness or disorder happens by mischance – from dental decay to lung disease, it's all a question of bad luck . . . It's clear, however, now that much more is known about the role of such things as diet, exercise habits and life style in the onset and progression of many disorders, that the passive swallowing of medicines will, in these cases, be seen as hardly adequate.[4]

Instead of fatalism we are offered a strategy to prevent just about any ailment; we are offered the new goals of 'positive health'[5] and 'radiant health'.[6]

We are told that each and every one of us has the capacity to be 'totally healthy'. And this is no matter of simply staving off the advances of illness and death. Total health is something to be actively pursued, a higher state than any of us has previously experienced. Total health will enable us to fight off diseases or to completely avoid succumbing to illness. And it is the responsibility of each individual to accomplish this new state. 'The active participation of the individual in the management of his life, so as to minimize the chances of developing some disease, or in the control or reversal of some disease processes, is very much in the vanguard of modern medicine and health care.'[7]

This aim of overall well-being has become linked inextricably with the idea of *preventative* medicine. We don't have to wait around to become ill; we can avoid illness altogether. If we do more for our health, we are told, we can avoid some of the major contemporary killer diseases. This commitment to a new state of total, positive or radiant health is a commitment which will infinitely extend the individual's involvement with his or her own health. 'You can't cheat death. But you can cheat ill health. Why wait until disease strikes? You have to work for health just as you have to work for most things in life. The Personal Health Programme can turn simply being well into vivacious well-being.'[8]

Wherever it appears this notion of total health signals an entirely new conception of health as something to be positively pursued. And with this new objective of perfect health has come a new set of messages for the individual, messages about the necessity for hard work and personal transformation.

In a fascinating essay Robert Crawford has described the findings of a research project into people's attitudes towards health, where this positive new concept of health became strikingly clear. None of the people interviewed were suffering from any 'treatable' illness. Yet almost all described themselves as 'not really healthy' on the grounds that they didn't do enough for their health. All had a clear sense that they could do more to achieve true well-being: 'I have a lot of thoughts about what to do about health. I have a view towards doing more things. But I don't do any of them at this point. I have to find time for it.' All the interviewees defined health as involving something more than just accepting the status quo; they required that the individual actively worked at health.

> I think generally we have to have a more healthy attitude. Health has to be a bigger part of our lives . . . I have to go back and take a look and change my life style. I have to find time for it . . . I think I have to be more concerned or excited about being healthier. My attitude now is passive. I am thinking a lot about it but I'm not really doing anything. I think I have to have more perseverance with the problem and make it a goal. Just like I have this goal for work, I should have this goal for health.[9]

Being healthy in these accounts is clearly only something which can be achieved through often difficult transformations of personal life. The only interviewees who described themselves as healthy were those who were actively doing something in the pursuit of health, 'I get exercise. I don't smoke, I don't eat a lot of red meat. I don't have a lot of cholesterol. I take vitamins. I get a physical every year. I think I'm healthy . . . I try to do all those things so I think that I'm healthy.' To be healthy in these accounts is a weighty matter. It is a state requiring work, commitment, possibly changes in life style. This commitment is required even if you aren't ill; total health should always be the aim because this alone will ward off illness and bring expanded possibilities in our life. Such views which permeate much of our contemporary understanding of health mark an enormous distance from previous views of health and the individual. Health is now a goal to be actively pursued, if rarely achieved, and it has become indelibly linked with individual attitudes, and individual commitment.

This new goal of individual well-being is always more than absence of physical illness. Increasingly, this new goal has been described as 'holistic', deriving its inspiration from the alternative therapies movement. Well-being is, 'this state of harmony, of wholeness, of health'. It is 'not just an absence of sickness. No! It is a dynamic state in which body, mind and spirit are aligned with one another.'[10] This integrated view of health is supposedly based on a new concept of the person or individual where the mind and body are no longer divided and treated separately. A person is 'mind, body and spirit' and the three parts cannot be separated. Therefore any approach to health cannot afford to concentrate on just one aspect of the person. This new approach to health is invariably presented as 'relaxed' and 'integrated', not putting too much pressure on an individual since it attends gently to all aspects of their life. Yet this new emphasis is actually extremely loaded. It promises an ideal state of perfectible health which can only be achieved if we are prepared to involve ourselves in a major process of self-transformation, not just of our bodies and our minds but even of our emotions.

The body can heal itself

The idea of a holistic approach which currently dominates popular conceptions of health derives from the alternative therapies movement. The alternative therapies movement has its own very precise version of the idea of the possibility of 'perfectible' or 'total' health and the necessity of 'well-being'. No less than with popular attitudes towards health there is a belief that very few of us have reached a state of true well-being since everything in modern life militates against this. There is a similar commitment to the idea that we can only really be well if we achieve a state of true, whole person, health. But the concept is often even weightier in the alternative health movement. Acquiring true well-being in this movement is sometimes presented not just as the possibility of becoming well, but often also of being 'healed', with all the connotations that carries from its previous location in religious discourses. This possibility sometimes goes well beyond staving off physical illness. It connects the prevention of, or recovery from, illness with finding a 'new person', a transformed person aligned with the healing properties of nature.

Within alternative therapies the possibility of well-being or total health is based on the idea of the natural health of the human body. This underlies the belief that there is virtually no 'illness' that cannot be overcome. In recent years, the alternative health movement has been making dramatic claims for its ability to deal with the diseases over which conventional medicine apparently has little control. For what is crucial in almost all alternative therapies is not the external disease but the question of an individual's overall well-being, the degree of natural health. This alone they tell us will determine the time taken to recover, or indeed whether or not the illness is ultimately fatal. Thus the disease as such is rendered secondary. Instead of a vision of medicine attacking the disease alternative therapies offer themselves as an alliance with nature, an alliance with the natural healing process of the body which they see conventional medicine as having so seriously neglected.

Positive health in these therapies is 'natural' health, that is, a hypothesized state which we would all have had at birth had modern life not conspired against it. This state of positive health does not just exist, a lucky gift for certain individuals. More frequently it is represented as a state achieved through hard personal transformations or through work with a healer or thera-pist. Indeed, in spite of apparent differences of technique, alterna-tive therapies share a sense of their work as liberating this natural force. It is a matter either of re-finding a lost state or of achieving a state which your body has never been allowed to experience. Whichever, the outcome will be the same. If the body can be helped on its way to true well-being, or real health, it will employ its own mechanisms of healing, either curing or fighting off even the most serious of the twentieth-century illnesses.

Many of the alternative therapies regard *all* diseases as poten-tially curable. The body, given the right conditions, will always try to heal itself. 'Anything that the body could regenerate, homoeo-pathy can encourage happening. Uterine fibroids can dissolve, brittle nails can go away. Herpes can disappear. All kinds of viral problems can abate. Aids. Obesity. Anything that the body can throw off, we have mechanisms against. The idea is just to stimulate the body and get those mechanisms working.'[11] Of all the alternative therapies, homoeopathy is probably the one most like conventional medicine in its claims for a system of medicines and treatments for specific ailments. Yet even here, in the words of a member of the Hahnemann Medical Clinic, Berkeley, we can witness claims similar to those of all alternative therapies. Ultimately, the whole of the complex system of homoeopathy is designed to reinforce the body's own attempts to cure. The patient is given medicine which copies or exacerbates the symptoms which he or she already has. Unlike conventional medicine, which aims at removing these symptoms, homoeopathy believes that they are the signs of the body fighting illness. Thus to treat 'like with like' will strengthen what the body naturally seeks to do for itself. It's a matter, one homoeopath told me, of helping the body's natural 'vitality' throw off the illness.

The idea that the body is self-healing is the common factor in a number of superficially very different forms of treatment.

> All the alternative therapies . . . rely on the principle that there is a vital force at work in the body, continually attempting to maintain the health and natural balance of your body whatever you throw at it and however you abuse it. When this inner vitality gets a little overwhelmed, it can look as though the healing has ground to a halt. Then an alternative therapy will give it a boost.[12]

Crucial in the various treatments is the idea of an innate or natural instinct for health which I discussed in the previous chapter. The body is assumed to lean naturally towards vitality and renewal, not towards degeneracy and decay. Yet this vital state of natural health is one which most of us have lost, either before birth or in a slow process through our lives. The various therapies claim to be able to help us re-find this inner force from which all cures must flow; 'healing depends on the action of the vital curative force within the human organism'.[13]

The ways in which alternative therapies promote this potential for healing are many and various, yet there is surprising consistency in this aim, summed up in the advertisement for a new natural health centre which will 'help you to find ways to encourage your body and mind's natural and inherent abilities to return to health and to remain healthy'. It is by no means only the apparently more fringe therapies which hold to the idea of the body's inherent ability to heal itself. I have already mentioned how the notion of cure in homoeopathy is based on the same principles. Similarly naturopathy, still following ideas formulated in the 1930s, believes that 'the body is always striving for the ultimate good of the individual'. In this account, all diseases have the same cause, namely 'the accumulation in the system of waste materials and bodily refuse, which has been steadily piling up in the body of the individual concerned through years of wrong habits of living'.[14] The cure consists of 'enabling' or 'empowering' the body to throw off this toxicity by a number of different measures, in this case by fasting, scientific dieting, hydrotherapy, or in conjunction with a number of other therapies such as herbal medicine or osteopathy.

These beliefs in the self-healing properties of the body have received an enormous boost from the importation (and steady growth) of oriental therapies, like acupuncture, acupressure and Shiatsu. These 'ancient' therapies, at least as they have been imported into the West, set enormous store on the capacity of the body to heal itself. Acupuncture and acupressure both stress how the work of their therapies is to release blockages in the flow and balance of the body after which the body will heal itself. The art of healing in acupuncture, I was told, is the location of bodily imbalances and the assessment of whether these imbalances have internal or external causes. 'The treatment will then allow the patient's own resources to cure the problem. More depends on the patient than on any other aspect of the cure.'[15] Similarly a reflexologist told me that the general idea is to free the body's own healing mechanism – it is 'enabling the body' rather than curing it. Shiatsu, increasingly popular as a treatment for stress and as a healing therapy, 'works on the body's own energy force. When somebody is ill, we don't just look at the symptoms, we look for the weak link in their energy flow and work on that weak link to create balance and restore the body's energy and its normal strong and powerful state.'[16]

Many of the 'Western' manipulative therapies work on much the same principle. They regard the 'faults' they find in posture, muscle or spine condition, as reflecting some inner problem, inhibiting the body's self-healing capacities. They aim to adjust bodily, 'structural' or postural problems so that general well-being can be released. Matthias Alexander, founder of the Alexander system of postural changes, described how reconditioning posture would realign the body and create overall well-being. We must, he said, 'appreciate the part played by an improving manner of use in the restoration and maintenance of psycho-physical efficiency and conditions of well-being'.[17] Chiropractors describe their therapy as a treatment of the 'causes' of diseases, understood as 'interference with . . . the nerves with subsequent nervous dysfunction whereby the body loses its ability to regenerate, with resultant disease'. When there is no interference, they go on to explain, 'natural self-healing maintains health'.[18] Kinesiology offers itself as a science of testing muscle response which allows assessment of imbalances in function. 'Imbalances are gently rectified by touch and acupressure massage. In this way energy balance is restored to the whole person mentally, physically and chemically, which encourages natural healing to take place.'[19]

The insistence that the body has a natural vitality and will to health could be endlessly duplicated. The idea is not exactly new – after all, several of the quotations derive from writers in the 1930s – but the alternative therapies movement has given it a new and extensive currency. The widespread acceptance of the idea of the body as 'naturally healthy' and the aim of releasing this natural health marks a new episteme, a new set of beliefs and 'knowledges' of the body. Views of the 'essential' state of the body have clearly changed. The body is no longer viewed as degenerate, subject to natural impulses, especially sexual impulses, which dragged man down among the animals. Nor is it the weak vessel, continuously misled by the temptations of the flesh. These were the views which dominated Christian morality in earlier centuries. Nor, indeed, is it the sexually free body of the 1960s, where sexual connection was essentially the most important self-expression of the body.

Instead, we have an essentially innocent body, born with wholesome impulses but gradually worn down by the hostile world. This is a vigorous body of perpetual renewal, the perfectible body which has no affinity to disease and to darkness; 'our natural birthright is radiant health, beauty, boundless energy, youthful vitality and joy throughout our lives'.[20] Through various therapies, working on the body and through an individual commitment to health, our bodies can be restored to their original state of well-being. It is almost as if there has been an exact inversion of earlier Christian views of mortality and degeneracy. There, the body was seen as part of the burden of being human. The body, inclined towards disease and death, was just part of mortality, the corruptions of material life. Only the soul could hope for perfection. Now the body is viewed as perfectible, and in acquiring that state of perfection, the individual will come into contact with an original state of well-being or health akin to Godliness.

In the alternative health movement, this original state of well-being and the one to which all activities aspire, is conceived of as a state of 'balance' and of harmony. Self-healing is possible if and when this state of balance can be restored, or found. And here we confront an apparent paradox. For if the body harbours this impulse towards good health, why should we ever succumb to illness at all? If the body, given the chance, will always renew and heal, why should chronic diseases exist at all, let alone be getting worse? Why should there be so much disharmony and lack of balance? It's as if, in order to posit this vital and renewing force, all things which cast a shadow, such as the evolution of the harmful virus *through* the human being, have to be denied. Needless to say, for the adherents to alternative therapies, this paradox is more apparent than real. They have a clear explanation for why nature should so frequently fail. But in order to understand this explanation, we first have to look more closely at what these vital, renewing and self-healing properties of the body are thought to be. What exactly is this state of vitality which is thrown out of balance? What is it that becomes impaired, 'unbalanced' and leaves us susceptible to diseases?

Again and again, we come across the same kind of answer from any number of different therapies. The natural health of the body, we are told, is balanced energy, and illness is the interruption of this balanced flow. The harmony of energies is the state which holds out the hope of perfect health and the end of disease. Yet this idea of natural health as balanced energies is, on close examination, rather curious. There are associations which cluster around notions of energy and refuse to be shaken off. These associations connect health with the economy of an advanced industrial society, anxious about its distribution of resources, and in particular with indivi- dual hard work. These meanings suggest that 'energy' is more than either a mystical or a scientific explanation of health. Perhaps it is also a metaphor, a highly appropriate metaphor for an advanced industrial society where the state of the body becomes the place where the concerns of the economy find individualized expression. It is to a closer examination of these meanings that we now turn.

The vital energies

'Energy' crops up in all the alternative medicines in one guise or another. For example, both homoeopathy and herbalism, which appear on the face of it to eschew the more esoteric mystical elements, include vital energies as explanations for the force of their cures. Homoeopathic medicine for instance is made by the process of potentization, a curious activity, which increases the 'potency' of the medicine the more it is diluted. One homoeopathic practitioner told me that however much he disliked the mystical element of alternative medicines, he could think of no other explanation for this curiously unexpected phenomenon than some build up of natural energies. Other accounts of homoeopathy are less cautious.

> After a degree of dilution . . . there is possibly no demonstrable molecule of the original material present. The potency of the medicine is said to increase with its progressive dilution. The latent energy of the substance is claimed to be released via this method of dilution, so that the effect on the body is related more to its energy patterns than to its physical characteristics.[21]

Herbal medicine, too, when pushed, sometimes accounts for the efficacy of medicines in terms of energy fields. '[Plants], in common with all living beings, have a non-physical energy field which may react directly on the "energy field" of people they are used to treat.'[22]

On the whole, ideas about life forces and energy fields are not just rather grudging elements, lurking at the bottom of these therapies. The idea of the fundamental energies of the body is explicit in most other 'alternative' ideas of illness and healing. The disruption of energies, their blocking and the resultant imbalance of the body are invariably blamed for illness or susceptibility to disease. Indeed, notions of balance and energy link up the more widely accepted alternative therapies like homoeopathy, naturopathy and acupuncture with those which are more easily dismissed as fringe. Yet even in the much more mainstream British Holistic Medicine Association, which explicitly seeks to collaborate with orthodox medicine, there are calls to recognize these views of vital bodily energies as fundamental to new conceptions of medicine: 'The teaching of medicine will need to place more emphasis on the flow of energies through the human body rather than be so exclusively concerned with the study of physical parts somewhat unrelated to the person as a whole.'[23]

One of the main sources of philosophical inspiration, or at least affirmation, for these ideas of the body as an energy system are the imported systems of oriental medicine especially those linked with Chinese medicine. Reflexology, acupuncture and acupressure all share ideas of energy meridians running through the body. All these therapies share the fundamental belief that 'the energy which the life force transmits is distributed through the body along a system of invisible channels or meridians. In normal circumstances, in a healthy person, the life force, *chi*, flows evenly, maintaining a balance between the vigorous yang and the restraining yin elements. But if either yang or yin becomes too dominant, the body's harmony is jeopardized and illness can result.'[24] Health exists when energy flows through the meridians or energy pathways in a 'balanced way', but either an 'excess' or an 'insufficiency', results in illness. Imbalance here refers to a very definite coherent philosophical outlook, connected with the Tao, where all aspects of life (people's characteristics, behaviour and all material objects) are said to express energies or balances of the essential opposites yin and yang.

Many of the esoteric and explicitly mystical alternative therapies have built on and adapted these 'oriental' ideas into their own system. These more marginal therapies offer themselves precisely as therapies which deal with energy imbalances, like Reiki, 'an ancient science of universal energy' which is a 'new age tool for healing and transformation'.[25] This 'science' is based on a technique handed down to special people who alone know the secret language which generates universal 'light vibration'; 'once the technique is learned, this universal energy can be used by us for promoting healing/wholing from within our body-mind-spirit dynamic.'[26] Radionics, similarly, 'is based on the principle that if the electro-magnetic fields now known to be associated with every human being are distorted by infection, injury, stress, unsuitable nutrition or other adverse factors, the resulting energy imbalance will manifest in physical illness.'[27]

For some therapies the field of energy is tangible, and perceptible to those who have skills to see it. Here these ideas of bodily energies have been linked up to long-held parapsychological beliefs. There is, for example, a resurgence of beliefs about human auras, those 'luminous areas surrounding people much as phosphorescence appears with sea creatures'.[28] Aura-Soma colour therapy deals with 'the colours surrounding every person as an electro-magnetic field which acts on the well-being and harmony of the whole body'.[29] The colour therapist will be able to assess the patient's state through a reading of his or her energy field expressed through her colour choices, and be able to recommend the colours with which to surround yourself. Kirlian photography regards the energy fields to be so tangible that they can be photographed with special equipment, 'allowing an easy visual diagnostic guide to your physical, mental and emotional well-being'.[30] The photograph will reveal how well the body is balanced by photographing the energy fields or auras around your hands – a different finger for each aspect of your personality.

Energy theories of health and illness tend to be accompanied by an insistence that the whole world is made up of energies. This is especially true of the fringe therapies where states of energy are offered as explanations for all phenomena. We have, for example, the Dulwich Health Society campaigning for people to sleep in safe places, that is, away from the 'harmful earth rays'. We also have dowsers who, with a variety of instruments, rods and pendulums, can 'read' the state of the earth's or a person's energy, a theory based on 'an energy interchange between the dowser and the object being dowsed through . . . a pendulum or other medium'.[31] One dowser, Bridget Carey, even goes so far as dowsing her shopping to determine the negative and positive values of food. 'Before choosing her fruit, vegetables, bread and other foods, Bridget dowses them, cupping a tiny silver pendulum in her hand and holding the other to her thymus gland while she concentrates on the question: will this be of benefit to me?'[32]

It is not unusual to find 'modern physics' quoted as an unexpected but welcome ally of these esoteric views. The theory of relativity in modern physics has suggested that all matter is interacting energy. In particular, modern physics has suggested that it is not valid to describe matter existing separately from those things interacting with it (hence the idea of relativity). Instead, any description must include reference to all that it interacts with, including the presence of the observer. The insistence on interacting energy fields has been taken up by the alternative therapies movement in highly selective ways. For example, many of the therapies have appropriated the idea that all matter is energy but they have grafted other meanings on to this proposal. What is most striking is the way in which these ideas of interacting energy have been given a more religious slant, pushing an abstract scientific concept of energy towards the idea of the world made up of positive and negative energies.

Yet there is nothing in modern physics to suggest that energy forces have negative and positive attributes. There's certainly nothing to suggest the almost moralistic interpretation which has been put on these energies, bringing on the one hand harm and disease and on the other, health and well-being. There is a whole world of difference, for example, between saying that 'matter is relative energy', and 'health is positive energy' or 'disease is negative energy'. The implications of modern physics are that nothing can be assumed to have fixed identity. Everything is process and transformation. Yet the appropriations of this idea of energy have exactly the opposite implications. Frequently, the alternative health movement suggests that there are things and states of being which express fixed positive or negative states. This is certainly true when it comes to understandings of the individual. There is a way in which modern physics could be read as having critical implications for our everyday understanding of individuals as having fixed characteristics which express their 'essence'. But as we will see in more detail in Chapter 4 this is the exact opposite of the views of the individual which dominate the alternative therapies movement.

Amongst other things, this view of the world as made up of positive and negative energies has spawned a whole industry of gadgets, machines and natural substances which can be used as 'mechanical aids' to revitalize our energy fields or detectors to gauge the state of our energies. Ionizers, for example, are there to deal with negative energy. Crystals are particularly favoured since vague 'scientific' evidence can be mobilized to affirm that electrical properties do exist in crystals. The result has been the promotion of the 'magical' properties of crystals or 'gem-elixirs'. Exorbitantly expensive Pulsor crystals can be used to turn away negative energies, defined in this case as deriving from all things electrical.

> Pulsors are semi-intelligent super-crystals literally able to change and amplify vibrations and auras of places and people. This healing activity of Pulsors manifests as an increased feeling of well-being, warmth, nourishment and safety from within an umbrella of soft, positive energy, that protects us from electricity, electro-magnetic pollution, negative energies and vibrations injurious to our life and from which we cannot protect ourselves by other means.[33]

These are the fringe elements of alternative therapies much derided by those inside and outside the movement alike. They have pushed ideas of energy in an explicitly mystical direction. Yet in many ways they share definite philosophical assumptions with the more respectable therapies. They have the characteristic amalgam of ideas about energies, percolated down from modern physics, and more essentialist ideas about energies and balance, diffused from oriental philosophies. But whereas oriental medicine sees complex interconnections between these energies, the Western therapies I have examined tend to imply models far more reminiscent of the good and bad energies of a Christian spirit world. In the hands of Western exponents there is often an intensely dualistic view of energies, linking up with magical and parapsychological views of negative and positive forces. Most abstract views of energy and the universe have been linked to the old dualisms of good and evil. It is a curious amalgam and one which suggests that the notion of energy should not just be accepted as a new 'scientfic' explanation of the body and its workings.

Many might want to attribute the emergence of this new concern simply to the fact that twentieth-century science has focused on energy and has therefore *proved* the importance of energy which has previously been overlooked. However, I think there are other reasons for the significance it has now in our sense of our bodies. For it has to be more than coincidence that a society such as our own has begun to talk of the body in the very language of advanced industrial society. Energy is a concept which belongs to an industrial society concerned with using energy for producing more and more. And, importantly, it is a concept relevant to the idea of creating individuals who are able to produce and consume efficiently. When it is applied to the idea of the body, energy appears as a metaphor for the kinds of productive relations which individuals have to an advanced industrial society. Especially when energy appears in the context of ideas of balance or harmony of bodily energies, it suggests efficiency, a metaphor of the body as productive, not wasteful or static, but in tune with its environment and expanding in productive possibilities.

The lack of harmony or balance is equally a metaphor, a metaphor for waste and lack of productivity. Ranging from the punishments of 'fatigue', and 'energy lows' through to the major diseases, wasted or blocked energy becomes distinctly 'wrong', a negative and unproductive state. Very occasionally this link becomes explicit: 'Is it any wonder that the health and productivity of a country go down when its greatest national resource, its energy is being squandered.'[34] It is as if the individual body has become the place where the anxieties of an industrial economy are played out. It is as if the individual was the point where the use of a country's resources were regulated, where productivity and efficiency could be decided. It is impossible not to wonder whether these new explanations of health and illness aren't ways in which the deep concerns of a capitalist economy are being carried into the individual's self-perception.

There are certainly ways in which this interpretation might be substantiated. Principally, one cannot fail to notice the way in which producing a balanced flow of energies has come to be tied up with the importance of individual hard work and commitment, a meaning which becomes explicit in a culturally more widespread concern with health, that is the health and fitness movement. But even in the alternative health movement, this metaphor of energies has become increasingly linked with the full involvement of the individual. For almost all the therapies believe that the release of 'positive energies' or self-healing properties will come through a healthy equilibrium involving emotional and mental levels, in short the involvement of the patient's whole personality in work to save her or his self. This might appear contradictory since in fact the role of the mediator or healer tends to be rather important in the alternative health movement. In the fringe therapies the mediation tends to be an elixir, a gem, or a new gadget. But even in the less mystical therapies, the 'healer' has a rather elevated status, considerably more elevated than the average GP. But this is not thought to be a fundamental contradiction. The work of the healer is explained as the intervention of a person or substance which can realign the energies of the body and release the capacity of the body to renew itself. It is up to the individual to help this self-healing take place. In short, the healer's contradictory significance is reduced by being presented as managing an interchange of energies.

Nowhere can this be seen more clearly than in spiritual healing which lies somewhere between the more respectable and scientific therapies and the more esoteric or fringe therapies. Spiritual healing is emblematic of the ideas of energy characteristic of a whole movement. It views healing as 'an exchange of energy', between healer and patient. The healer's potential, we are told, depends on using her/his body as an instrument. The aim of spiritual healing is to channel energies, both transmitting positive energies to the patient and channelling negative energies away from the patient's body. It is disease or damage in the body which gives off negative energies. The skill of the healer depends on the 'quality of "light" which she is able to bring through and transmit to the patient.'[35]

Spiritual healing stresses the fact that no one actually heals anyone else; the success depends on the exchange of energies between patient and healer. The patient's own willingess to be cured, we are told, is crucial in releasing the flow of energy. The patient is told both to be open towards helping the healer, and to do some work helping her or himself. 'Learn to think positively and creatively about restoring your bodily health and about peace of mind' is the sort of advice to be expected here. Matthew Manning, Britain's most famous spiritual healer, even expresses unwillingness to treat those who are not fully committed themselves to the possibility of self-healing. This emphasis on the role that the individual has to play in his or her own cure is, if extreme, typical of the philosophy of achieving health in alternative therapies. While the aim of all therapies is to intervene and work on 'blockages' to the flow of energy, thereby releasing natural health and self-healing, nevertheless, all these therapies stress the active role which the patient must play in effecting a cure. Whatever the therapy, personal responsibility invariably has a very high premium as an element in restoring or maintaining good health. 'The responsibility should be more and more turned over to the patient through changes in life style, with the physician taking a secondary role.'[36]

Indeed, it is impossible to talk to anyone on this subject without them raising the fact that responsibility for health has shifted from the medical professional to the individual. 'In recent years holistic approaches to health care have called attention to the role of the patient in the healing process, and primary responsibility for health maintenance has shifted from the medical establishment to the person.'[37] The element of personal responsibility in achieving or maintaining good health is stressed by all these therapies; it is only with the full participation of the individual that health can be achieved and all those who turn to alternative health practices are warned of the involvement that will be required of them: 'one of the most challenging and difficult aspects of preventative medicine is that it puts much of the responsibility for health onto the patient.'[38] Only with this involvement can we really hold out hope for true well-being, a well-being which will be of tremendous transforming potential, not just of our own lives but of our surroundings too. 'We can change and grow,' announces one book; 'it is up to us to take responsibility for making the changes in our lives that will enable us to contribute to the well-being of the whole.'[39]

Health and fitness

It is when we come to look at the appearance of these more holistic views of health in popular representations that some of the underlying meanings become rather clearer. In particular, the link that has increasingly been made between health and fitness has brought to the surface the implications of regulating energy and the central responsibility of the individual in this regulation. 'Total health' has also become the new objective of a widespread concern with fitness. And few could fail to notice that at the same time as fitness has picked up new meanings, it has become something of a cultural obsession. 'Gone is the old image of sport as something to be watched from the terraces or from an armchair in front of the television. Indeed a new survey . . . indicates that those who take part in sport outnumber those who watch it by five to one.'[40] Even for those of us who are still part of the armchair-bound minority, it is pretty well impossible to avoid the impression that you *should* be reforming your ways.

In this popular view of fitness, there are very great rewards promised if total health can be achieved. 'Fitness, both emotional and physical should be the goal of anyone who desires an energized and productive life.'[41] And what is this fitness? 'It's more than just the absence of disease. It's a feeling of all-over well-being that generates from good joint flexibility and muscular development, from healthy lungs and heart stamina, and from the ability to exert reasonable stress on the body with positive, re-invigorating results.'[42] Quite precise changes can be expected. 'A stronger heart. A more agile body. A trimmer figure. Better skin tone. A clearer, more alert mind. These are the golden rewards of total fitness.'[43] It is not uncommon to find promises that not only will we increase energy, stamina and endurance, but that we will actually live longer. Regular bouncing for example 'is thought to retard the process of ageing, even reversing it . . .'[44]

The new goals of fitness, like the goals of alternative therapies, are now considerably more than just absence of physical ailments or a better body. Most important is the promise of that highly prized acquisition – energy. In popular discourses on fitness, the key terms are 'invigorated', 'energized', 'enthusiastic'. Unlike previous concern with dieting and losing weight, the emphasis is now on *acquiring*. Total fitness is about acquiring more rather than denying ourselves. It offers a horizon of expanding possibilities rather than diminishing ones. Fitness is no longer simply about maintaining stasis within the body, but about increasing and expanding the body's capacities. It offers us more from life, even sometimes quite literally, in suggesting health programmes might allow us to eat more because they will speed up our metabolism. In this respect the state of health offered by becoming really fit is a state where we will be able to produce more and consume more.

And there's a further acquisition to be had – a better attitude to life. There is a distinct implication that this new fitness will benefit all aspects of the person, including emotional life and mental outlook. Raquel Welch for example promotes Hatha Yoga because 'it maintains her body, her mind and her emotions in peak condition.'[45] This is the new integrated view of health which lurks behind contemporary talk of fitness. Here we are told that mind and body are inseparable and that to become fit will inevitably benefit our mental and emotional states as much as it benefits our physical health: 'In the next few years you may find yourself going to your exercise class for the sake of your mind as much as your body.'[46] This is the new '3-dimensional approach to health' as Blue Band Margarine declared as they launched their booklet on 'Food, Fitness and Feelings'.

Unlike the views of energy in the alternative therapies movement, these views are unequivocally expansionist, self-enhancing and acquisitive. The difference between the two movements is a significant difference but it is nevertheless one of degree. In the alternative therapies movement the concern with the balance of energies seems to express a concern with regulating the economy. It is a concern which potentially at least could open up on to the more political questions of the depletion, and the unequal distribution, of the world's resources. The health and fitness movement has no such implication. It is about expanding the capacities of an individual as producer and consumer. The difference between the two movements is the difference between concern about a regulated economy and unregulated competition where there is no sense of anxiety about resources.

Not surprisingly, these more overtly 'capitalist' messages connected with the health and fitness movement also express views of personal involvement with well-being. And again what can be seen is an extreme version of capitalist views of the necessity for self-discipline and work to fund production and consumption. This may seem surprising given that on the surface at least, new concern with fitness might appear more egalitarian and hopeful than previous concerns. Previously, anxiety about transforming the body had been focused almost exclusively on women. And the form that concern had taken was exclusively with 'getting rid of' or 'shedding' extra pounds in order to make the body conform with prevailing highly restrictive ideals of the female body. With the new developments of work-outs, aerobics, jogging, and so on, there's an apparent shift to health, including emotional health, instead of beauty and sexuality. This shift is apparent even in the beauty industry itself. Anita Roddick, owner of the Body Shop, refuses, for instance, to advertise using pictures of glamorous women, or to mention beauty. Instead her products are sold as 'natural' and 'healthy', and advertising emphasizes, 'cleansing, polishing and conditioning' rather than beautifying.

Thus there might appear to be a shift towards a more egalitarian, and less controlling, concern with the body, where both men and women are equally touched by the imperative to transform themselves. Fitness in these popular accounts is almost invariably offered as an integrated package, designed to reshape your whole life and not just your bottom (although of course there is always the covert promise that overall fitness will in fact happily yield the perfect figure). Explicitly at least, reshaping is about transformation of life style. It requires new attitudes towards food, and towards reducing the stresses and strains placed on the body and mind by everyday life. But by far the most important requirement is a commitment to the hard work of getting healthy.

Significantly, in the concern with health and fitness, the form which this work takes is exercise. Indeed, exercise is the privileged mode by which an individual can acquire total health and achieve 'a creative energy that allows us to greet each day and its tasks with confidence and enthusiasm'. It isn't so very long ago that 'keep fit' classes had an embarrassing ring to them. They conjured up notions of portly middle-class women doing gentle exercises to stave off the inevitable middle-age bulge. Anything more vigorous took on decidedly militaristic and therefore unfashionable over-tones – such as physical education. Bending and stretching, flexing the muscles, serious running were all activities which could only have two possible aims – either to join the army, or to become a PE teacher and take perverse pleasure in making others follow your example.

All this has changed. Physical fitness has become something to be admired and envied, an ideal to which we should all aspire. Everywhere we are encouraged to see the virtues of exercise and its reward of fitness. The militaristic overtones seem to have disappeared with the gentler and more glamorous sounding activities like aerobics and jogging, to be backed up by a generally 'healthier' attitude towards life. The combination of reducing stress, new eating habits and exercise is promised to generate more energy. But exercise, even with its new-sounding names, is no less punishing than before. Even integrated into ideas of the overall health of the person, there's a clear message that exercise will require hard work, self-control and discipline before the rewards can be reaped. 'The discipline experienced in self-mastery gives you a sense of freedom and autonomy.'[47] Control and *self-discipline*. The words that are used give the game away. To achieve fitness we have to follow *routines* and *regimes*. With a little *discipline*, they tell us, we can establish a pattern of exercise which will yield fantastic results.

No less than previous regimes of physical fitness, these new approaches carry distinctly self-controlling and masochistic implications. At some health spas, we are told, 'you work hard – but your body loves it.'[48] All the people who are held up as shining examples describe a structure requiring phenomenal hard work and commitment, but bringing great benefits to attitude and energy and, above all, a sense of self-achievement and self-control: 'Some people think I am obsessive. I'm not. I just know that I need to keep running because it's a way of keeping myself feeling good, more positive, more in control.'[49] And it is by no means coincidence that the movement has spawned its adherents to pain, embodied in Jane Fonda's 'going for the burn', or in the marathon mentality where marathon participants are encouraged to pass through the pain threshold. A strong link has been forged between fitness and endurance. In these quarters 'fitness' has been hegemonized by notions of bodily fitness which require self-discipline and will-power. And just as before, it is women who are particularly susceptible to this call for fitness and health (from which, hopefully, beauty will follow). Yet the concern with fitness now carries a distinct, additional, message: health has to be deserved, and can only be acquired through individual hard work.

Conclusions

In the 1980s there has been something of a reaction to overtly masochistic notions of health. The more moderate, 'holistic' notion of health as a state of being involving all aspects of the person is much more commonly encountered, even if it is often subordinated to a concern with exercise. Nevertheless, the implications of these more masochistic concerns are not insignificant. They show the way that the new concerns with overall well-being and perfectible health are being mediated into a wider consciousness which is more explicitly concerned with health as something to be attained through hard, sometimes painful work and generating guilt when it is not achieved. Implanted in that popular consciousness is the promise of health as the guarantee that we can enjoy ourselves in an ever-expanding capitalist economy.

Well-being, then, has very great resonances within both wide-spread popular conceptions of health and fitness and within the alternative therapies movement. Although it is to be achieved in different ways, there is widespread agreement on the possibility of perfectible health with a concomitant end to disease *and* the necessity for the hard work of self-transformation. In the fitness movement this perfectible health is simultaneously expansionist and self-disciplinary. The privileged route to both expanding energy and the route of greatest self-discipline is exercise. Thus fitness is still linked with outward manifestations of the self-discipline which is now thought to be necessary in achieving health. Within alternative therapies, true well-being has somewhat different, although related, meanings. True well-being is linked to views of liberating natural health, and finding a balance of energies. Its rewards will be the possibility of healing in a sick society, either in the form of fighting off illnesses or in a more mystical sense of a transformed and well person.

In both of these manifestations of concern with perfectible health, energy is a crucial concept. Within the push for greater fitness, more energy is the reward. Within alternative therapies, energy is more ambiguous, sometimes implying acquisition and expansion, but sometimes expressing an anxiety about resources in an advanced industrial and capitalist economy. In both its manifestations, however, the metaphor of energies as the explanation for health and illness expresses a concern with wastefulness and inefficiency, with illness marked out as wasteful and unproductive. There is, by implication, a suggestion that health is efficiency.

This metaphor of productive energies has increasingly come to be linked with the full involvement of the individual. This is not just through spectacular displays of self-improvement which characterize those associated with fitness, but increasingly a healthy equilibrium is thought to involve emotional and mental levels, the involvement of the whole personality. Indeed it is these meanings which are beginning to dominate the more popular sense of the need to improve health. Increasingly, even for those not directly involved with alternative therapies, these are the meanings which are coming to dominate contemporary notions and expectations of health. Health is 'well-being', a state to be won back or achieved. It will involve the whole of ourselves and be our salvation but its success will be our personal responsibility.

It might be asked *why* personal responsibility should have become such a big issue in alternative health care. For it is quite possible to conceive of a model of bodily energies which has little or nothing to do with the individual and his or her emotions and intentions. Indeed, some of the Eastern medicines, such as Vedda medicine, so admired within alternative therapies, are extremely fatalistic. Health in these medicines is not to be won by the hard work of an individual but through the skill of the healer. In order to understand the way in which the West has foregrounded personal responsibility, we must confront the question of 'holism' so crucial to these changed attitudes towards health. For it is through the concept of holism that alternative approaches to health express their views of the role and responsibility of the individual in his or her own health. And it is also in the concept of holism that we find answers to the further puzzling question of why if the body has a will towards health and self-healing do so many of us fall ill? It is to these questions that we now turn.

Notes

1 Brochure for the Institute of Optimum Nutrition.
2 Mark Plater, 'Acupuncture and the State of Wholeness', *Green Farm* magazine, vol. 1, no. 4, 1986.
3 Editorial for new Health page, the *Guardian*, June 1988.
4 Sandra Horn, *Relaxation*.
5 Dr Bircher-Benner, in Janet Pleshette, *Cures That Work*.
6 Kenton, Leslie and Susannah, *Raw Energy. Eat Your Way to Radiant Health*.
7 Horn, op. cit.
8 Institute of Optimum Nutrition, op. cit.
9 Robert Crawford, 'A Cultural Account of Health' in J. B. McKinlay (ed.), *Issues in the Political Economy of Health Care*.
10 Plater, op. cit.
11 Quoted in *Homoeopathy Today*, 1986.
12 'A–Z of Alternative Health', presented with *She* magazine.
13 Manifesto of the British Naturopathic and Osteopathic Association 1987–8.
14 Harry Benjamin, *Everybody's Guide to Nature Cure*.
15 Interview with acupuncturist.
16 *Alternative Medicine Today*, Summer, 1986.
17 Brian Inglis and Ruth West, *The Alternative Health Guide*.
18 Leaflet on Chiropractic.
19 Inglis and West, op. cit.
20 Shakti Gawain, *Creative Visualization*.
21 Leon Chaitow, *Vaccination and Immunization*.
22 Barbara Griggs quoted in Inglis and West, op. cit.
23 Evarts G. Loomis, 'New Dimensions in Healing' in the *British Journal of Holistic Medicine*, vol. 1, April 1984.
24 Quoted in Inglis and West, op. cit.
25 Barbara Ray in the *International Journal of Holistic Health and Medicine*, Summer, 1985.
26 ibid.
27 Information, the Radionics Association, Banbury, Oxfordshire.
28 Inglis and West, op. cit.
29 Information leaflet on Aura-Soma Colour Therapy.
30 Interview with practitioner of Kirlian photography.

31 'Dowsing', *Green Cuisine* magazine, September 1986.
32 ibid.
33 Advertisement for Pulsor crystals.
34 Malcolm Hulke, *The Encyclopaedia of Alternative Medicines and Self-Help*.
35 Lecture on 'Spiritual Healing' at the Festival of Mind, Body and Spirit, 1987.
36 Loomis, op. cit.
37 Frances Vaughan, *The Inward Arc*.
38 Horn, op. cit.
39 Vaughan, op. cit.
40 *Sunday Times* Lifeplan Supplement, March 1987.
41 Earl Mandell, *Shaping Up with Vitamins*.
42 ibid.
43 Advertisement in *Shape* magazine.
44 Advertisement in *Lean Living* magazine.
45 Article in *Healthy Living* magazine, September 1986.
46 Article in *New Health* magazine, September 1986.
47 Christopher Connolly and Hetty Einzig, *The Fitness Jungle*.
48 Advertisement for a health clinic.
49 Quoted in the *Sunday Times* Lifeplan Supplement, op. cit.

3 The Fantasy of the Whole Person and the Question of Personal Blame

Virtually all alternative therapies claim to be 'holistic', that is treating 'the whole system rather than the parts'.[1] The claim is that, unlike conventional medicine, holistic approaches see health as the well-being of the whole person, and therefore involve not just a fit body, but a well mind or spirit. Holism has wondrous associations. It conjures up visions of a medicine which is preventive, gentle, and natural. This is an approach to the body that will not assault, attack or maim. It offers to integrate bits of our life, and bits of our bodies. Unlike conventional medicine, it will not increase our sense of fragmentation by treating bits of our bodies or different symptoms as if they were entirely separate from each other. Instead, holism suggests the possibility of integration, of feeling that all parts of ourselves belong to the same essential person and have meaning in relation to one another. Holism has almost religious connotations, suggesting that the whole person can be found and that when it is, the individual will be healed. 'To heal is to make whole. And what is whole can have no missing parts that have been kept outside.'[2]

'Holism' is the great strength of the alternative health movement. A holistic approach to treatment tends to mean a quality of personal attention and care which is total anathema to orthodox medicine. What is more, this holistic approach also appears to give an individual an unparalleled sense of participating in, perhaps even controlling, his or her own well-being. Yet this profound conviction that lying within each and every one of us is the kernel of a whole person is not without its own problems. Quite apart from the fact that the idea of a whole person might be a fantasy, there's a way in which the attempt at integrating all parts of a person to one central core has eased the way for a potentially highly moralistic approach to health. By relating the state of the body, the level of stress and so on to a deep meaning expressed by this kernel of the whole person, everything is made comprehensible by reference to this inner core. In the idea of the whole person, the possibility that an individual has control over health and the possibility that an individual is to be blamed for disease often shade into one another. And there are numerous ways in which a holistic approach to health gets tipped towards this more guilt-provoking idea of illness.

Holistic treatment: emotions and medicine

The precise definition of what is a holistic approach to health seems to vary a great deal between practitioners. Some talked of holism as simply the ability of an individual to integrate different treatments for different needs, such as using herbal medicine for a specific ailment, Alexander technique for working on body and posture, and psychotherapy for emotional distress. A small minority emphasized the social implications for the term holism; they stressed that holism implied the links between individual and environment and suggested treatments which would not only balance the internal parts of an individual but would also balance the relationship between the individual and her or his environment. More generally, however, practitioners and consumers alike defined holism as the treatment of the 'whole person', an approach which refuses to separate body, mind and spirit. Virtually all spoke of the tremendous difference which this approach actually made to *treatment* where a high premium was put on individuality and on exploring a whole range of aspects of an individual's life which conventional medicine would usually ignore.

There can be little doubt that this emphasis on the 'whole person' has produced techniques of treatment which diverge radically from most people's experience of routine consultations with conventional doctors. Almost all of the alternative therapies, apart perhaps from those which involve 'healing techniques at a distance' (e.g., radionics or diagnosis by hair), ask extremely 'intimate' questions about the individual involved. Consultations with many practitioners of alternative therapies involve detailed questioning about individual background, family history, history of illnesses, tastes and preferences, and current life situation. This individuality is frequently taken into account in the treatment. No two individuals should necessarily be given the same treatment. The healer or therapist must determine the individual's general state of physical, emotional and spiritual well-being before offering treatment.

The attention to the individual has been held by both supporters and critics of alternative therapies alike as one of its major strengths. Unlike conventional medicine, often overstretched in resources, and riven by professional divisions and hierarchies, these holistic therapies appear to offer a highly personalized approach to health problems. The founders of the Holistic Consciousness Foundation included amongst the reasons for the growth of popularity of alternative approaches to health those who turned to it 'seeking a re-assertion of individuality. These are the patients who refused to be categorized as an NHS number and wanted to be treated as an individual.'[3] More cynically, one interviewee described his sessions with an alternative therapist (acupuncturist and masseur) as just plain good value. For £15 he was given a solid hour's hard work on himself; he felt known and recognized as an individual.

But what exactly are these forms of attention to the individual which make alternative therapies so attractive, and how do they relate to the overall philosophies of health, well-being and disease? Time has always been cited as one on the main ways in which alternative therapies truly attend to the individual; whereas conventional doctors might see a patient for five to ten minutes, alternative therapists regularly see their patients for an hour or an hour and a half. They ask questions about changes in emotional state, and seek to find out about the apparently most minor physical symptoms. They want to know what we've been eating, how much exercise we have been doing, how much energy we have and how we are feeling. But it is more than just a question of time. Other factors include physical contact. Clients for Alexander technique, Shiatsu, or even a simple massage, all describe the experience of 'knowledgeable' hands holding, exploring, guiding and shaping the body, providing a wonderful sense that something is being done to help your body and overall well-being in a most tender and comforting way.

But perhaps most significant in the claims made for a whole person approach is the way in which emotions are integrated into treatment. This is particularly obvious in therapies based on some kind of medicine, as opposed to, say, manipulative therapies. In many cases this integration of the emotions is quite subtle and submerged, glimpsed in questions about patterns of mood, sleep and energy. But there are some practices for whom the emotions are absolutely central, like Bach flower remedies and aromatherapy. It is these therapies which most forcibly underline the distance between alternative and conventional medicine. In these practices it is far more common to find remedies offered according to a specific set of emotions or a personality type than it is to find the treatment of a specific illness. Bach flower remedies, for instance, offer thirty-eight remedies divided into seven groups to cover 'all the known negative states of mind'. The groups are fear, uncertainty, lack of interest in the present, despondency and despair, over-concern for the welfare of others, loneliness and oversensitivity. Thus a practitioner is likely to prescribe clematis for 'daydreaming and indifference, inattention and escapism' or chicory for 'possessiveness, self-pity, craving attention'.[4]

More than anything else it is this attention to moods, emotional states and predispositions of the personality which inform the idea of 'whole person' treatment. Examples could be endlessly duplicated but the following description of a homoeopathic approach to diagnosis could speak for a movement, 'all humans consist of the mind, body and spirit and all should be examined by any treatment. All patients should be treated as individuals, so diagnosis cannot be standardized. A diagnosis should be arrived at by examining all facets of a person's life; background, physical type, emotional state, body language, clothing etc. This creates an overall picture, that of the "whole person".'[5] Here then are all the aspects of a person which conventional medicine has regarded as irrelevant. Previously consigned either to psychotherapy or to astrology, and definitely considered irrelevant to the state of the body, they have now moved into the centre of the picture.

No one could deny the way in which conventional medicine overlooks personal and emotional factors which are likely to produce or foster illness – distress about poor social conditions, personal problems, and so on. Yet this new attention to previously neglected areas of the individual goes much further than simply including concern with all the factors in an individual's life as they are mediated through the emotions. The notion of the whole person very often merges indistinguishably with the concept of personality, or personality type. Homoeopathy is occasionally quite explicit about this. Its remedies are directed towards certain types of person with characteristic emotional states and often characteristic physical ailments: 'If you know your medicines very well and their mental and physical aspects and you know the mental make-up of the patient you can predict what his physical disease is going to be like and the other way around. If you know the physical make-up of the patient you can know what his temperamental nature must be.'

There is the very clear suggestion that medicine itself has definite emotional profiles, as if there were certain negative and positive emotions in nature which express themselves in persons and plants. This article from *Homoeopathy Today* goes on to give examples. The medicine, Arsenic album, for instance, is 'by nature very fussy, very meticulous'. The typical patient for Arsenic album 'is called the gold-headed cane patient – very trim and proper and the top of his cane must be well-polished.' At one level homoeopathy deals in personality types, offering constitutional medicine which is matched to the patient by the symptoms it produces. The Ignatia patient, for example, 'is a victim of modern society. Excessive social excitement and involvement exhausts them. Unlike the Sepia patient who is dull and stupid, the Ignatia personality is clever, highly refined, gentle and educated.'[6]

Much of this cannot fail to stir memories of the humoural medicine of the Middle Ages, which at its simplest classified people according to four distinct personality types and treated all ailments according to these dominant personality types rather than the characteristics of the disease. Obviously it is harsh to draw these links with homoeopathy which is based on longstanding research into the effects on the body of various substances and which combines elements – characteristics and symptoms of the illness with the personality type of the patient – in arriving at treatment. But nevertheless it is important to recognize the forceful return of beliefs in 'constitutional' medicine, and of course, by implication, beliefs in the existence of definite constitutions or personalities as crucial factors in any diagnosis.

This reintegration of constitutions or personality types into medicine is not without some obvious problems. The very idea of a personality type tends to disregard social and cultural reasons for the differences between individuals and their reactions. Instead people are seen as having been born with fixed constitutions, certain predispositions and tastes which make up their essential being. This view of the individual lends itself all too readily to certain kinds of mysticism and it is no coincidence that, side by side with the 'respectable' medicines like homoeopathy and acupuncture, flourish the more arcane pursuits like astrological medicine. Indeed astrology in general is enjoying a second wind, under the protection of some alternative therapies. This is a practice which is founded on the idea of a limited number of personality types. And, unlike constitutional medicine, astrology has no hesitation in explaining the origins of these different personality types: it is all down to the arrangement of the stars at the moment of our birth. But if most of the therapies which use constitutional medicine would turn away from the idea of heavenly conditioning, nevertheless the prevalence of beliefs in personality types has left a space for the more mystical explanations of personality to flourish.

There appears to be something of a contradiction in the understanding of personality in these approaches to health. For a 'whole person' approach to medicine stresses the degree of control an individual can exercise through her or his ability to change. Yet beliefs in personality types tend towards fatalism. If you accept the idea that we are born with an essential constitution it is difficult to see how far individual actions are going to be able to change this basic inheritance. Most of the therapies do not *appear* fatalistic, that is they do not seem to say that you are born as you are and can do nothing to change it either because of inherent, inherited, or astrologically conditioned characteristics. On the contrary they appear to be offering remedies for change, arguing that personality type is merely one predisposing factor. Yet, as we shall see, the idea of personality type is actually extremely important in these new approaches to health *and* it sometimes carries with it associations of a static and limited model of a world of fixed emotions and personalities into which human behaviour, characteristics and illness can be fitted. In fact, the unresolved tension between calls for change and beliefs in fixed personality types has tended to be the way in which guilt-provoking and moralistic notions of illness have been able to grow.

Spirit, sickness and personality – the end of the germ

Ideas about the personality, understood as emotional predispositions, are very often concealed in references to holistic medicine's attention to the 'spiritual side' of individuals. Although the idea of personality is very often submerged like this within alternative therapies, it is nevertheless an absolutely crucial and linking concept in explanations of why individuals become ill. According to all practitioners or proponents of alternative therapies, one of the major failings of conventional medicine is precisely its lack of concern with the spiritual state of the individual who seeks help. It is almost impossible to meet with definitions of holism which do not include criticisms of conventional medicine for its neglect of the more ephemeral aspects of an individual. The neglect, we are told, is due to 'the materialism' of conventional medicine. On closer examination this criticism invariably refers to the way in which conventional medicine pays no attention to the emotions of the patient. In other words it is almost the same criticism as that made about neglect of the personality.

Holistic approaches regard their own concern with ephemeral aspects of emotions and spirit as being an entirely new conception of the 'individual'. Most stress that they refuse the division which previous approaches to health operated on. These separated the body and its workings (medicine) from the mind (education, intellectual debate, reasoning) and from the spirit (emotions and religion). Holistic approaches to health tend to refer to these more ephemeral emotional factors as the individual spirit. Even Larry Dossey, often critical of the alternative health movement, bases his ideas on the 'spiritual bankruptcy' of conventional medicine. 'The mention of the word spirit, immediately causes the deepest furrowing of the scientific brow. Eyes are averted in the direction of the measurable and the precise when spirit announces itself . . . Yet for all the problems in addressing such a murky concept, all of us in medicine know privately it is a notion that has never died and that will never die.'[7] Dossey goes on to describe the death of an old man, rebelliously smoking to the end, as irrefutable evidence of the importance of the spirit. The old man's personality was such that, although dying in horrific circumstances, he always retained his sense of the pleasure and satisfactions of life.

The example is typical. What is described as the 'spiritual side of man' very often refers to the same things as 'the personality'. There is an extremely hazy area between spirit and personality in references to the whole person. Yet the slide between the two is not insignificant. For although, in the past, connections were made between illness and the spiritual state of an individual, there has never before been a theory which connects illness with the state of the *personality*. The connection between illness and personality gives an individual an even greater responsibility for his or her illness than previous 'religious' explanations of illness as expressions of God's displeasure. It is, of course, a gross distortion of the facts to suggest that all previous approaches to illness and health did separate 'the spirit' and the body. It may be true of medicine in the twentieth century but this period is the exception rather than the rule. Almost all the religions of the world contain a strong discourse on the connection between illness, health, death and the spirit world. Traditional healers believe in the idea that a sick person is one whose spirit has been in some way infected. Christianity is no exception especially Catholicism where contact with saints and relics offers cures. Christ himself performed miracles on the sick and dying implicitly promising that with faith, illness could be overcome. And there is plenty of evidence that, in more directly superstitious periods, people regarded illness as a sign of God's disfavour, thereby linking the state of an individual's spiritual life to the state of that individual's health.

On the whole though, at least in Western societies, disease was not particularly personal. Disease was more about the state of humanity than the failures of a particular individual. It could be argued that with the emergence of 'rational' medicine, the individual was for the very first time, definitively let off the hook in terms of making a necessary connection between the health of his body and the state of his spirit and morality. With claims for a precise 'scientific' understanding of disease as an external virus caught by any individual who came into contact with it, it was hard to make an individual feel directly responsible. Yet here in alternative medicines, we find the re-awakening of beliefs in the connection between the life of an individual and the health or sickness of the body. The more subtle writers in the field of holistic medicine like Patrick Pietroni are keen to stress that they are not returning to an era of religious superstition, 'to accept a spiritual cause to health and disease would be taking us back to the bad old days of witches and shamans' incantations and burnings from which Descartes and Newton saved us in the seventeenth century'.[8] He insists that it is merely a question of life style – illness and recovery being connected with the mental and spiritual attitudes and satisfactions connected with that life style.

His caution is highly necessary. For far more frequently are met glib assertions of the link between spiritual and physical well-being. For many holism heralds a new era, where the link between spirituality and individual health can be fully recognized. And good health will only be restored when the whole person is 'in harmony':

> . . . holism deals with the total human organism – an integrated whole which is greater than the sum of its parts – rather than just symptoms, viruses and illness. Holism understands that a person whose mind, body and spirit are in harmony, whose energy is in balance, does not manifest dis-eases. Holistic healing thus focuses not on getting rid of symptoms but on empowering the individual to establish a state of mental, emotional, physical and spiritual harmony and well-ness in which health is a constant of life.[9]

The notion of dis-ease in this quotation gives the game away. In this approach there is no such thing as a disease with an existence separate from the individual who manifests it, a disease which can be contracted regardless of anything which the individual might do in the face of it. There is only a state of imbalance, or blocking of essential energies, which allows an illness to take root and manifest itself. 'If organs of the body and body systems are either congested or deprived of their vitalizing energy known as CHI, for any length of time, it predisposes them to a condition of dis-ease or malfunc-tion.'[10]

There is no more widely used quotation in the alternative therapies movement than that of the microbiologist René Dubos who wrote, 'There are many circumstances, some of which are common occurrences in human medicine, where the physical, chemical and physiological, and probably psychological factors which affect the host play far more decisive parts in the causation of the disease than does the presence of this or that micro-orga-nism.'[11] What seems to have completely disappeared in these accounts is that vision of the germ in the blood, or the virus in the system, an entity so tangible that children used to be taught to sneeze behind their hands, with the warning 'coughs and sneezes spread diseases'. Even the common cold is a question of susceptibi-lity, and factors predisposing the body to hosting the virus. Now the talk is of 'psycho-incubation', something within the individual which will allow her or him to fall ill. And crucial in this disappearance of 'disease' is the reappearance of personality, albeit disguised as 'the spiritual side of man'. It is the state of the whole person, the spirit or personality which predisposes an individual towards illness. But the differences between earlier 'spiritual' accounts of illness and contemporary accounts based on the idea of personality is that the individual is much more directly and personally responsible for illness.

Most practitioners would insist that they are not creating 'guilt' for illness. In other words, they argue that personal responsibility for getting well and a predisposition towards illness do not amount to a moral condemnation of an individual for falling ill. Many proponents of alternative therapies insist that these ideas of disease, of the imbalance of the body and the predisposition towards illness have no critical implications for the state of the individual who falls ill. Indeed much of the writing in alternative therapies concentrates precisely on all the likely 'external causes' for contemporary ill health. Yet the implications of this personal responsibility are often unavoidable as we shall see. Not only does the alternative health movement have a very clear hierarchy of the significance of external factors in causing illness, but we will also see that time and time again, personality features as an explanation for how external factors are mediated into the individual body and affect illness and recovery. It is through the idea of personality, and the possibilities for harmony and disharmony within the personality, that an unmistakable whiff of a morality of health and illness enters the alternative health movement. 'What is sown must be reaped; hence the degree of health regained or maintained is proportionate to how closely one can or will follow the rules.'[12]

What is sown must be reaped: the question of cause in holistic therapies

One of the fundamental attractions of a holistic approach to health is that it asks the question of the *cause* of illness. And by asking this question there is an implicit assertion: we don't just have to accept and live with illness. We can find a cause and eradicate it. The commitment to finding a cause of illness is, of course, the logical conclusion of the belief that the body will always seek good health and try to restore itself. If disease has no objective existence and 'health is the normal natural state of the human being'[13] then it is not possible to think of energy imbalances as just spontaneously happening. Because of the idea of original natural health, alternative therapies are committed to a theory of the origins of diseases.

The alternative health movement is strewn with accounts of the 'true causes' of illness or the 'deep causes' of illness. Unlike previous diagnostic procedures which were aimed at understanding the organic nature of the disease, the diagnostic practice of alternative therapies involves a whole picture of the patient's life and a search for why that individual has become ill. Instead of the doctor as reader of the signs in the body, in which the individual's life was irrelevant, the diagnostic activity must now search into the social, environmental and emotional background to the disease. And because there is a rejection of the idea of the external, non-discriminatory existence of the disease, then the quest for the cause of illness will inevitably focus on aspects of the individual's life which could be altered. 'Emphasis in therapy should be directed toward the actual causes of illness rather than the mere relief of symptoms. This will increasingly involve consideration of the whole person: body, mind and spirit, the emphasis being directed through the reinforcement of natural immunity rather than attack on the disease state.'[14]

This focus on the idea of illness as a state of *dis-ease*, that is, lack of ease, in the body has important consequences for how the cause of illness is theorized. For if disease is not external and arbitrary but the result of individual susceptibility, then what are the favoured causes for this lack of well-being and the resultant inability of the body to withstand disease? Within the alternative therapies movement there is an implicit but quite definite series of preferred explanations for why people lose a state of well-being or ease and become ill. And it would be no exaggeration to describe these explanations as ultimately belonging to a hierarchy, in which certain causes are favoured over others. At the top of the hierarchy is stress, the twentieth-century ailment *par excellence*, and the factor which gives the notion of personality type such pre-eminence within current views of health and illness.

It would be easy to overlook the significance of stress since the first explanation for illness that you tend to meet in the alternative health movement is 'modern industrial society'. Industrial society is a full assault on natural health; our bodies are attacked from outside by pollution and radiation, and from the inside by the use of additives and chemicals in food and medicine. As George Vithoulkas, 'the world's leading homoeopathic physician', has put it,

> The whole ecology question and the pollution in which we are living, is unbelievable. But even more important is the inner ecology of the body. We introduce drugs into our bodies all the time: countless drugs, every day new ones, and food which is polluted with hormones and chemicals . . . It's grotesque but it's a fact: if tomorrow the pharmaceutical companies that make all these heavy drugs were to go bankrupt and stop producing them, and leave the population without any, what you would see in this society would be terrible; shouting, fighting, aggression, madness, fits . . . panic. But then you would see the real picture of what our state of health is![15]

In this characteristic vision, conventional medicine is firmly on the side of modern industrial society, almost in a conspiracy against health.

Conventional medicine crows about its successes in improving health and the importance of modern technology, whereas alternative therapies regard the general possibilities for real health in an entirely different light. 'Never mind the statistics that say we are living longer; look at the heart diseases, the cancers and the chronic diseases, and now Aids. We are facing a big problem here, but nobody seems to take it seriously. Maybe nobody is giving them the facts.'[16] As far as the alternative health movement is concerned there is a major health crisis. Although mortality rates have fallen, general health is a lot worse than previously, 'the graph of chronic degenerative illnesses is high and climbing higher. One in four people will die of heart disease. One in five will die of cancer. Survival rates for the commonest cancers are virtually unchanged from those of a quarter of a century ago, but the incidence of both these diseases has rocketed.'[17] And alternative therapies have no hesitation in linking this health crisis to the hazards of the twentieth century – pollution, bad diet and stress.

It is worth mentioning again that these ideas were in circulation earlier in the century. In the 1930s Dr Max Gerson described cancer as

a disease of society, a disease of life style. He listed the over use of artificial fertilizers and chemicals in the soil, the over-refining and adulteration of food with toxic additives, the poor preparation of food and the pollution of our environment generally as being individual factors which combined to adversely affect the body's function as a whole. He postulated that over a period of time these factors weakened the body's resistance to a point where one final trigger-factor produced localised symptoms.[18]

Yet when Gerson first wrote on the subject, his was no more than a lone voice in the wilderness, and regarded as a very cranky one at that. Now these are the very ideas which dominate alternative therapies. Cancer, they say, and most other chronic degenerative diseases, *do* have identifiable causes.

Almost all the alternative therapies believe that these identifiable causes lie in the remoteness of modern life from nature. Many regard the poor diet of contemporary times as the major source of illness, 'naturally well-being can't be achieved overnight. It's a gradual step-by-step process. (So is feeling poorly: most people are born healthy and gradually eat themselves ill.)'[19] Others insist that the pollution of our environment and planet is responsible for these malignant attacks on our bodies. This pollution is not just from major hazards such as radiation from nuclear testing or nuclear accidents. It is also the 'pollution' of the technology of modern life,

> On top of the [radiation from nuclear testing] there are luminous clocks and watches which glow with radium. Worldwide, they expose people to four times as much radiation as emissions from nuclear power plants. There are luminous gunsights, exit signs in cinemas. Uranium used to be used to make false teeth shine and there are still thousands of people walking around with radioactive teeth. TV sets emit X-rays. An X-ray in hospital would expose the patient to about 100 micro-Sieverts. A Sievert is a unit of effective radiation. The lowest recognized dose at which cancer may have been induced is 65mSv.[20]

But far and away the most important explanation for this general health crisis of the twentieth century is the more nebulous but no less invasive cause of illness, stress. Stress is the pre-eminent health problem of the late twentieth century, a problem which hardly even had a name previously. One elderly psychiatrist told me that in the past people used to describe their general depressions and miseries as 'nerves'. Now the key concept is stress. Her experience is symptomatic. Stress and lack of general well-being are now inextricably welded together. The nature of stress and stress-related illnesses is the subject of endless books and talks. You can read about 'Stress in Your Life' or 'Identifying the Stressors'. Conversely the number of books offering advice about how to relax and overcome stress weigh down the shelves of books on self-help health. While the external hazards of modern life may be the oft-quoted causes of contemporary illness, it is invariably stress which tips the balance from being well to being ill.

The crucial stress factor

Stress is often understood as purely 'external', that is, the stress which chemicals and pollutants put on the body, or just the stress which modern life generates. Yet stress is also an aspect of all the elements of an individual's life. Stress is a 'composite of personal, social, and physiological upheaval'.[21] It is because stress is both an external and an internal factor in these theories that it solves one of the important problems in the view of disease in alternative therapies. Certainty about the harm done by modern technological society has one main drawback. Why is it that not all of us fall ill with cancer? How is it possible if we are assaulted with these side effects of machines and chemicals that some people manage to lead long and apparently healthy lives? It is here that we find the important space for the idea of stress. We are told that it is our ability to withstand the stresses of modern life which determines whether or not these assaults of modern life will be mediated into our body as disease. Stress, more than any other term, seems to me to be synonymous with these new movements for personal health and well-being. For stress is understood as something which varies from individual to individual and can be controlled according to the emotional type of an individual. Stress is thus offered both as the explanation for why some individuals are susceptible to disease, and as the chance for a cure, the area where we can make significant changes in our life.

In these accounts the reason why stress is so chronic for modern man is that our nervous system is geared to producing a physical response to life-threatening dangers when that response is no longer appropriate.

> Nowadays we are likely to feel stress and the sense of urgency and danger in situations which do *not* demand an intense burst of physical activity, but the automatic nervous system still responds to threat by preparing us for it. Modern stresses are more likely to impinge on us in the form of . . . the close proximity of fast-moving traffic, or unexpected bad news, or the anticipation of an angry quarrel. In such cases, intense bursts of sympathetic activity with its accompanying subjective feelings of fear, anger, agitation, may be far from helpful.[22]

Virtually every self-help book on health takes this view of stress. It is the product of a redundant physical, natural response – the widely cited 'fight or flight' response – which is no longer possible in our complex modern society. Instead we internalize these responses as emotions. And it is the difference in the quality of these internalized emotions which decides whether or not an individual will fall ill.

There is a curious, but widespread, agreement amongst all the commentators that stress is much worse now than previously. Modern life, it is agreed, is infinitely worse than anything which mankind has previously had to face. Somehow it is implied that the stresses of continuous factory work, poverty, and the death of several children were less severe than contemporary stresses. I certainly find this extremely hard to accept. For unless one imagines that people of a previous era just didn't feel as much as ourselves, then it is impossible to imagine that they would have been unaffected by the terrible hardships, sufferings and loss characteristic of earlier periods. In fact, behind the idea that it is much worse in the twentieth century lie two assumptions. One is that we are physically weakened by drugs and chemicals. The other is that people of previous historical epochs had more appropriate outlets – rituals, support of their communities, and so on, which enabled them to externalize rather than internalize these 'stressors'. Certainly the second of these is something of a presumption. We just don't know how much support was given to individuals or indeed whether philosphical or religious fatalism was of the remotest comfort.

This is hardly an objective assessment of stress but rather a strong and prevalent fantasy of ourselves as victims and not beneficiaries of the twentieth century. Stress is both the ultimate horror of modern society and also the vital mediator between the outside and the individual, that which decides the degree of illness or health. The very concept of stress implies an interlinked mental and physical response. The inability to cope with external stress is usually seen as the outcome of too much internal or emotional stress. And with this we have come back full circle to the issue of holism. For it is the concept of stress which allows the idea of the involvement of the 'whole person' in their illness and their health to work. Susceptibility to disease is understood, in the last instance, as the degree to which stress is at work, and whether or not we can successfully dissipate it.

Stress is the crucial interlinking concept of holism, the factor which explains how external influences in health are translated into differential individual reactions. Stress is fundamental to the claim of alternative therapies that disease is an internal event, an external manifestation of our inner being: 'I believe . . . that people construct circumstances for themselves which they then react to with stress, that is, they are not being stressed by external events beyond their control but are stressing themselves.'[23] Stress explains how ill health can be *our* responsibility. Whatever the more cautious exponents of the links between mind and body across the terrain of illness may say, there is a clear consensus that disease is 'self-created and self-cured'.[24] The position of stress at the top of the cause-of-illness hierarchy makes it clear how these assertions are possible. How we handle stress is an individual thing, and that alone will ultimately determine the course of an illness.

The cancer personality

If stress is able to produce susceptibility to illness and disease we confront again the question of why some individuals are susceptible and not others. And here the concept of personality returns with full force. Personality, emotional reactions and predispositions determine the way in which individuals handle stress. Nowhere could these links be clearer than in the discussion of cancer in the alternative therapies movement. For several years now there has been a strand of argument that insists that emotional factors are crucial in determining which person will ultimately succumb to the illness. It is the degree of stress to which an individual has been exposed, and his or her ability to withstand that stress, which will determine whether or not cancer will take hold. Thus stress and personality are closely linked in the alternative therapies movement. Personality is almost like a lightning conductor. A certain set of attitudes and a certain kind of emotional predisposition will be able to earth stress and not be destroyed by it. An unbalanced or blocked person will not be able to handle stress and the illness will take hold of their bodies. 'Managing stress both through restructuring false beliefs and by learning relaxation techniques, can greatly reduce our susceptibility to illness.'[25]

Several eminent researchers have gone so far as to insist that there is a 'cancer personality', the person whose life circumstances, and general emotional outlook will predispose her towards getting ill and influence her ability to get better. Thus bereavement or divorce might be common occurrences, but they become life threatening if the individual is too repressed to express feelings of anger and loss. The denial of anger seems to be an emotional state particularly favoured as the cause of cancer.

> Very frequently, in cancer patients, [a] rigid pattern of behaviour revolves around attempting to be as other people want them to be rather than as they personally feel they should be. This commonly leads them to try and please other people, to do as others would want them to. There is often an overtone of passive subservience. They are not the types to become aggressive or anti-social. They want to be liked.[26]

The 'cancer personality' in these sketches is riddled with anger and hostility but unable to express this anger, turning it in against itself. Someone with a 'cancer personality' has too highly developed a sense of what society wants, in other words he or she is, by implication, a conformist, someone who has internalized all the damaging repressions of our society. Although the sketches of such a personality are rarely explicit about sexuality, they carry the implication that the cancer personality is also sexually repressed, being too sensitive to the standards and expectations of society.

This picture of a typical cancer personality is one that has been carried over to several of the chronic degenerative diseases like arthritis and multiple sclerosis. Thus we now have the typical arthritic personality: 'Rheumatoid arthritics were extremely dependent, felt inadequate, had difficulty coping with their environment and with other people, and were severely blocked in emotional expression . . . They avoided closeness, were aware of strong, unexpressible angry feelings, reacted over sensitively to the slightest criticism or rejection, and tended to court other's favours.'[27] In exactly the same way as with the cancer personality, the arthritic personality is said to be repressed, particularly in anger and sexuality, a person who has too effectively internalized damaging social values. As Susan Sontag has pointed out in *Illness as Metaphor*, although many of these descriptions are presented sympathetically, they do not add up to the personality most valued at this stage in the twentieth century. These are the social failures, the victims who are not able to express themselves and their 'inner needs'.[28]

Thus a picture begins to emerge of diseases with 'meanings'. They are the manifestation in the body of things that are sadly wrong in a person's life, in particular damaging attitudes or a repressed personality. Cancer is often seen as having a very direct personal 'meaning'. The cancer has taken hold because of things that have gone wrong in your personal life. The only way to save yourself is through total transformation, an eradication of previous life style and a completely changed attitude. Cancer here is a disease of life style, the symptom of a life that is unbalanced and not 'whole'. And if attitude is significant in susceptibility to disease, it is certainly all-important in recovery from disease. In the recovery from cancer, everything, we are told, depends on attitude, state of mind, and will to live. 'In his work, Professor Doll gives the claim of medical authorities that 85 per cent of all cancers could be prevented by changes in life styles.'[29] Publishing is now littered with monuments to the triumph of the will, accounts of miraculous and heroic struggles against cancer, such as *You Can Conquer Cancer*, and *You Can Fight for Your Life*.

Certainly, the role of will-power and mental attitudes is presented as all-important in overcoming illness. 'The patients' belief system, their hopes, fears, expectations and their level of well-being drastically affect the outcome of any treatment.'[30] At one level, this might appear as just good sense. It seems obvious that a positive attitude towards recovery is liable to be more successful than a negative and depressive one. But there are many adherents to the alternative health movement who have gone a great deal further in their views on individual responsibility for illness, in terms either of a person's susceptibility or of their ability to recover. For some, dying is a defeat, a sign that individuals cannot transform themselves. Thus one writer tells of a woman who abandoned her therapy and fairly swiftly died of cancer.

> She was also a very envious woman, full of anger, despite the fact that she regarded herself as being good and kind. If she had not abandoned analysis, she would probably still be alive today, because to this date we have never had a patient die from any disease, no matter how serious, while undergoing analytical treatment. This leads us to believe that the individual who truly accepts analysis has decided to live. The patient who abandons treatment does so because he has already given up on life.[31]

If the person is a 'whole' person consisting of mental, physical, emotional and spiritual parts, any of these can cause the body to go wrong. Yet there is, in fact, very little equality between these various parts. The ephemeral qualities of mind, emotions and spirit – the personality – are the privileged causes of illness.

> Our health is a . . . manifestation of our internal state of consciousness – of course, not just our physical well-being but our emotional, mental and spiritual well-being as well. This leads to the understanding that any healing, if it is to be anything more than symptomatic, originates in consciousness itself. It follows that all illness, or lack of health . . . can be seen as psychosomatic.[32]

Psycho-incubation, a term widely used, sums up this approach. Attitude and state of mind provide the fertile soil in which the seeds of disease can grow.

An 'unbalanced' attitude can lead us into pursuits harmful to the body, like smoking and bad diet. The ill person is the person whose life is out of balance, whose mind and body are not in harmony, the person who is not 'whole'. Those who will be cured are those who have strength to transform their life and their attitudes, those who can become whole. 'Those who nearly die, return to take control of themselves as never before, often dedicating themselves to "right living" and to a positive healing path.'[33] There's a clear belief that those who really want to be well can be. They can discard their disease, no longer needing it if they can transform their emotional habits, '[My disease] went away of its own accord after some years, and I've never had an itch of it since. And I know why. Because I have no further use for it.'[34]

Of course none of this need imply that the person is weak who either succumbs to illness or cannot recover. After all, the odds are, as we have heard, stacked against us in the twentieth century. Yet somehow the whiff of moral failure attaches to these ideas and refuses to go away. In spite of this insistence on the hazards of modern life with the likelihood of many of us becoming ill, alternative therapies often make quite clear that illness and recovery from it are decided by the attitude which an individual has to life. Such views have tended to generate a heroism around recovery. Those who do survive serious illness are those who have taken control. I have even, on two separate occasions, heard alternative practitioners talking about how they wished that they personally had had cancer, so convinced were they of the power of determination and changed life style in fighting the disease. They had wanted the chance to prove how important their strategies were for achieving well-being, a well-being so total that it could even throw off cancer.

The morality of being ill or well

The impression that something is being said about morality and personal strength arises not so much from any direct statements about the illnesses themselves as in statements about what it is to be healed, what it is to be well. To be well is to be 'whole', to have all your parts and aspects of yourself in balance, to be in harmony with yourself and others. Healing in one of the earlier quotations I used was even called 'wholing'. 'A person whose mind, body and spirit are in harmony, heals themself.'[35] Of course no one actually says that a well person is a good person – indeed that isn't quite the implication either. But, if health is wholesome, it is clear that the well body expresses a morality, an attitude. And in a milieu like this clearly a sick body, a neglected body, is a sign of something mentally or spiritually wrong. This is not a simple world of evil and good, where those with cancer are tainted with Satan's mark. But it is a world where individual intentions, strength of will and commitment to a life style which is right and harmonious have their rewards in visible good health. And it is a world where wrong attitudes – neglect of self-expression and needs – have their punishments. It is a world of heroes and victims.

In this account of disease and illness there is a strong sense that the body itself has become a sign, a sign which announces the attitudes of an individual. A sick body is a sign of something wrong; the body's weakness in the face of disease demonstrates that the individual was not integrated, balanced and harmonious. Worse still, certain diseases can be seen as evidence of a whole range of negative emotions, repression of sex and anger, self-denial and an over-developed concern with social pressures. A healthy body, on the other hand, particularly a body which has 'recovered' from a major illness, is a sign of achievement, of having found harmony and balance in attitude, and in the case of those already ill, of having triumphed by transforming themselves. Disease and illness have become in this movement inextricably linked up with attitude and personality, expressing a morality of strength versus weakness, harmony versus disharmony, negative versus positive emotions.

There is a strong sympathy for religion in the whole alternative health movement so that it would be no insult to it if I described this philosophy of health and the body as profoundly religious. However I'm sure that I imply different things. The more esoteric and mystical elements within the alternative health movement have a view of man as a spiritual being, and spiritual or religious experience as an experience of one-ness with the universe. Spiritual and physical harmony are to be achieved through the pursuit of this one-ness, and this one-ness is largely to be achieved by remaining in touch with 'the natural'. 'The fundamental cause of all dis-ease, no matter what its form or symptoms, is (with the exception of conditions foreign and inimical to human life) the violation of Nature's laws.'[36] However the religious quality of these ideas derives from a very precise religious discourse – that of Christian puritanism.

This may seem a strange comment since so many of these therapies explicitly reject the 'repression' of Christianity, and ally themselves either with a more pantheistic spiritualism, or with the mysticism of oriental religions. However, much of the entangling of health and morality and the implication of personal responsibility for well-being, is more than tainted with puritanism. In these accounts of a life out of balance and the process of healing are all the exact elements of 'the salvation of the soul' much beloved by Christianity. Here is a version of the sinner whose life has to be saved, and is saved through the agonizing spiritual crisis of turning to God or Jesus. Many of the alternative therapies involve a relinquishing of previous ways of life (diet, sexual repression, body habits). Often the process of healing involves a version of a spiritual crisis. Like religion's dark night of the soul, numerous alternative therapies warn of a healing crisis, 'withdrawal' in dietary changes, a 'low ebb' in psychotherapy or a 'healing crisis' in homoeopathy. The body, we are warned, will get a lot worse before it can get better. 'Following treatment, some reactions may occur as the body strives to remove toxins from the system and the elimination systems may become more active resulting in a form of "healing crisis".[37]

The outcome of this crisis, this change of life style and attitude, is, as I have said, the whole person. It is the person who is 'pure', who pursues a wholesome diet, whose outlook on life is 'whole'. But instead of the pure spirit, who will enter the gates of heaven, we have the wholesome body. It is as if the afterlife has been won in the course of our own individual lifetime. We have gone through the breakdown, the crisis and the re-integration. We can now enjoy the afterlife on earth. The body and its well-being has become the major site where individual attitude, strength of will, and commitment of wholesomeness can be expressed. And those who have recovered from the major diseases of our time are held up as the heroes and heroines who literally embody the way in which this spiritual state can be won in our own lifetime.

The myth of a whole person

The ideology that there is and should be a whole person sustains the alternative health movement and its ideas of well-being. Within the movement, there is no doubt that wholeness can be achieved. No one seems to question for one instant that becoming a whole person is both desirable and possible. As we have seen, actual definitions of wholeness are hard to find. At its most general, a whole person tends to imply one who is balanced, in harmony, who attends to all aspects of their well-being, that is their body, mind, emotions and 'spiritual' needs. A clearer idea of what exactly a whole person is tends to emerge by implication rather than explicit description. A whole person does not have a 'negative' emotional state, that is, he or she does not carry around unexpressed anger or envy. By implication the whole person has left such emotions behind once they have been expressed. Whole people are able to deal with stress, using it creatively; they do not allow stress to incapacitate them. Above all they have a 'balanced' personality, a personality which mediates stress and allows the person to cope with the extremities of modern life without getting ill.

Yet it is possible to argue that the idea of a whole person is a total fantasy, and a fantasy which belongs significantly to this particular historical moment. Many philosophers or theorists have stressed that the idea of an 'integrated' person for whom there is no inner conflict is a complete illusion. In the past this illusion was a lure held out by religions; now it has been taken over by the health movement. Freud was convinced that the 'person' was always riven with contradictory feelings. Indeed, the very notion of the split between conscious and unconscious thoughts was based on the idea that certain feelings and thoughts were unacceptable to the conscious mind and were relegated to the unconscious. From that it followed that the unconscious 'cohabited' with the conscious, always looking for ways to express itself, get its way and contradict the conscious intentions of the individual. Freud's most famous examples of the contradictory nature of the individual are contained in his work on dreams and in what has become known as the Freudian slip, both instances in which the unconscious is shown to be seeking expression, often disturbing and horrifying the individual with its suggestions. Thus Freud deduced the Oedipus complex from the evidence of dreams concerning the desire to kill a parent, dreams of individuals who on the surface loved and respected their parents.

Of course, Freudian analysis assumes that unconscious material will find its way into consciousness. But he had no such illusion of integration, of healing, of bringing all parts of an individual's existence into line with some core truth about the personality. As far as he was concerned individuality was always a precarious construct, liable to conflicting and contradictory impulses. The modest aims of early Freudian analysis were merely to allow the individual to live more easily with the contradictions. How different all this is from the dream of the whole person in alternative therapies. Here, contradiction within the person is *impossible, intolerable*. A person subject to inner contradiction is the person who will be sick. 'All levels are interconnected and a state of "dis-ease" in the body is always a reflection of conflict, tension, anxiety or disharmony on other levels as well.'[38]

Conclusions

Although the fantasy of the whole person is now located in views of health, it is in fact the dominant fantasy of personality in our culture. Influenced by Christian ideologies, Western society has always tried to sustain a view of the personality as having an essence or inner truth, which explained all aspects of behaviour and emotion. In particular there has always been an attempt to link this view of the personality to morality, to the existence of good people and bad people. Everything which happens to an individual is ultimately to be explained by their own actions and therefore their personal responsibility. It is not hard to see the ways in which this has been translated into the body and health, where the whole person is the person who will not become ill, and the unharmonious individual is the one who will be susceptible to disease. It is extremely hard to avoid reading an article on health these days that does not stress that we have responsibility for our own health, and that we can choose to be well or sick. Indeed, we can even choose whether we live or die. It is as if disease has itself become a kind of morality, demonstrating the level of the individual's personal control over their life.

This is not a world of original sin, in which there is no forgiveness. It is a world where the state of well-being or wholeness can be pursued and won by hard work. But there are still fundamental beliefs that the individual has a true essence and that this essence will somehow be the deciding factor in what happens to that individual's life. Thus views about the external pressures which modern life places on the individual are really secondary to the belief that the individual is ultimately responsible for whatever happens to him or her. Although views like Freud's have been influential in the twentieth century, at some very deep level there is enormous resistance to the implication that the individual subject is fundamentally contradictory, without any fixed essence. And there is even greater resistance to the idea that the individual has very little power to influence the exact course of his or her life.

It is surely not too far-fetched to suggest that the resurgence of ideas of wholeness and inner essence is a reaction to the way in which individuals had been a trifle absolved from personal responsibility. It seems that the more thinkers in the twentieth century explored the possibility that the individual is contradictory, and that society, or the external virus, not the individual, is responsible for the bad things which happen, the stronger the reaction has been. At the very moment traditional religious and moralistic views of the personality began to lose a hold intellectually, they have regrouped around health. And under concern with the body and health, these ideas of the coherent, whole individual and the consequent morality of personal responsibility have extended themselves even more deeply into people's self-perception.

Of course, this is a highly problematic argument. Many within the alternative health movement would see my ideas as symptomatic of a contemporary materialistic malaise, which leads to passivity, despair, and a sense of personal powerlessness. But my questions will not go away. Does the active involvement of the individual in determining the course of their life have to be won by swallowing a moral code where blame attaches to the failure to be healthy in body and mind? Does a sense of control and responsibility have to be focused on internal transformations, and behaviour adjustments? Or are these, in fact, one way in which people will remain out of control of the major *social* decisions which affect their lives? In the chapter which follows, 'The Consciousness Industries', we shall see more precisely what is at stake in the drive for change and behavioural adjustment which is offered as the way to save ourselves and improve the quality of our lives.

Notes

1 Patrick Pietroni, *Holistic Living*.
2 *A Course in Miracles*.
3 Interview with Douglas and Nina Ashby of the Holistic Consciousness Foundation.
4 Quoted in Inglis and West, op. cit.
5 Interview conducted at the British Holistic Medical Association.
6 *Homœopathy Today*, Summer, 1986.
7 Larry Dossey, *Beyond Illness*.
8 Pietroni, op. cit.
9 Jason Serinus, *Psychoimmunity and the Healing Process*.
10 Information brochure on acupuncture.
11 Quoted in Leon Chaitow, *Vaccination and Immunization*.
12 Moule, op. cit.
13 ibid.
14 Loomis, op. cit.
15 Interview with G. Vithoulkas, the *Guardian*, July 1986.
16 ibid.

17 ibid.
18 Ian Gawler, *You Can Conquer Cancer*.
19 Brochure of the Institute of Optimum Nutrition.
20 'The Age of Radiation' in *Green Farm* magazine, op. cit.
21 Horn, op. cit.
22 ibid.
23 John Harrison, *Love Your Disease: It's keeping you Healthy*.
24 ibid.
25 Michael A. Weiner, *Maximum Immunity*.
26 Gawler, op. cit.
27 Weiner, op. cit.
28 Susan Sontag, *Illness as Metaphor*.
29 Gawler, op. cit.
30 Harrison, op. cit.
31 Claudia Bernhardt Pacheco, *Healing Through Consciousness*.
32 *Green Farm* magazine, op. cit.
33 ibid.
34 Norman Lindsay, *My Mask*.
35 Serinus, op. cit.
36 Moule, op. cit.
37 'Reflexology'. Information issued by the Bayley School of Reflexology.
38 Gawain, op. cit.

4 The Consciousness Industries

In a recent book on well-being,[1] we are given a list of possible ways in which we can reduce stress. One would be exercise which would provide a 'temporary release'. Another would be to use drugs but this would have tremendous risks. By far the most effective way, we are told, is to 'change your personality'. This might sound like a tall order but apparently not. 'Personality is learned behaviour, and so, like bad habits, can be changed and unlearned at will.' Such views are absolutely typical of the movement I am describing. If stress, and therefore susceptibility to illness, is decided by our personalities, then the logical way in which we can get better or stay well, is to ensure that we have a healthy personality. 'Personality' features as a giant slumbering beneath the surface in holism's explanations of well-being and illness. So it should come as no surprise to find that natural therapies have created a space in which a number of 'psycho'-therapies, designed to change the personality or consciousness, have received an enormous boost in popularity.

Whever you find the likes of reflexology, nutritional therapy and herbalism flourishing, there too you are likely to find various therapies of the mind, like Gestalt therapy, transactional analysis, co-counselling, humanistic psychotherapy. These therapies are linked with the alternative health movement not as a necessary or integral part but more as fellow travellers. Each has it own history, and all have an origin and place in a general history of the development of psychotherapy in the twentieth century. Yet with the growing popularity of natural therapies, these psychotherapies have taken on an entirely new life. More to the point, their explanations of mental problems and how changes are to be achieved have come to dominate accounts of the mind and consciousness within alternative therapies. The dominance of these explanations of consciousness is not without its problems. As we shall see in this chapter, the explanations are far from value free, having distinctive ideologies both about how easy changes are for the individual, and about what is wrong or undesirable in a person. They are ideologies which ultimately advocate behavioural adjustments to the existing society, adjustments which promise a heady mixture of health and materialism: the individual will be happier, healthier and more successful.

Changes

In the culture that surrounds alternative therapies there is strong disapproval of 'artificial stimulants'. Caffeine, drugs, alcohol and sugar are often regarded as representative evils of modern society, generating artificial highs, addiction, and depleting the body of its natural strengths. Drunkenness, 'tripping' and the infamous hyperglycaemic highs are all taken as symptoms of a person sadly out of touch with his or her body and therefore its natural resources. A person who needs these things is not a well or whole person. There appears to be a world of difference between these views and those of the culture from which the alternative health movement is supposed to have emerged, the hippie culture with its positive search for 'altered states' or heightened consciousness and awareness.

There's an apparent paradox here. For although those involved with this new concern with health scorn any 'artificially' induced altered states, nevertheless the aim of transforming consciousness and heightening personal experience is absolutely central to the whole ideology. Indeed I would go so far as to say that, when it comes to what should be done about emotional or mental well-being, the aim of transforming or altering consciousness is perhaps the dominant personal ethic of the health movement. Along with the call to save ourselves with a change in life style and diet, comes the requirement that we change our consciousness and our emotional life. Consciousness, understood as our mental and emotional predispositions, has assumed a front-row seat in new attitudes towards health.

Of course, there is nothing specifically new in the idea of the mind and body being connected in illness and health. I have mentioned earlier the whole connection of disease with sin and evil. And even in the early twentieth century Freud tentatively suggested that some physical symptoms may have their origins in psychic problems repressed in the individual's unconscious. He called these psychosomatic illnesses. But psychoanalysis and its derivative forms of psychotherapy are still extremely cautious about how far to stress this link; they are still happy to allow an objective reality to disease and illness which has little to do with emotional well-being.

But notions of the connections between the mind, illness and the possibility of healing, as we have seen, have lost much of this caution in the alternative health movement. The current surge of interest in therapies aimed at transforming consciousness has occurred precisely because the alternative health movement promises health if we can change our mental outlook. Sometimes these therapeutic changes even become the basis of an offer of personal salvation, as in this one for Pre-Creation or Soul Therapy.

> Through this system a person is able to make contact with his Soul or Divine energies, literally rejuvenating his whole being. In this expanded state of awareness he is easily able to release deep-seated blockages. Not only from this life, early childhood traumas etc., but also from other incarnations. This therapy also helps most physical-emotional-mental-psychic, and sexual conditions.[2]

Other therapies might not be so committed to previous incarnations but there is something typical here in the convergence of the language of psychotherapy with promises of new spiritual and physical well-being. And transformation of the consciousness, with its linked aspects of behaviour and emotion, is centrally offered as the route to this healing.

The philosophy of personal consciousness, illness and healing is absolutely dominated by the belief that we can and *should* make changes. One glimpse at the books which dominate American and British non-fiction publishing makes it clear that change is the order of the day, whether it be our weight, our unfortunate personal habits like smoking, our phobias, or our stress levels. 'How to' and 'you can' books are frequently best-sellers. Making changes has become a massive cultural preoccupation and certainly a full-time leisure pursuit for some people as they jog away their flab, and breathe themselves into states of deep relaxation. On the surface at least it appears as if there is no such thing now as fatalism; none of us is irreversibly determined as something or other; we can all make changes. And more importantly we *need* to make changes.

Even if *how* we can achieve changes varies dramatically from therapy to therapy, there is remarkable consistency in the belief that it is possible for a person to change. Most of the psychotherapies clustering around natural therapies promise to facilitate change. Courses from the Hypnothink Foundation, for example, 'enable you to change your own life for the better . . .' The Rebirthing Movement offers 'a significant emotional transformation brought about by insights, new thoughts and understanding of life and oneself'.[3] Indeed, the ultimate goal of many of the therapies is 'restoration of the freedom to change'.[4] Each therapy holds the promise that we can change and puts enormous positive value on making these changes. Everywhere we can attend courses for self-fulfilment, self-assertion, self-management and self-awareness, all states to be achieved through changes in our basic selves, our consciousness. In the significantly named *Frogs into Princes*, Neuro-Linguistic Processing is introduced as teaching us the *processes* of human communication, which allow us to understand how we can make significant changes to our own processes of communication. 'It is possible to describe any human activity in a detailed way that allows you to make deep and lasting changes quickly and easily.'[5]

Within these views there is an apparent commitment to the infinite pliability of the human mind and personality to become something other than what it currently is. The person in these ideas is at least theoretically free to change: 'A human being and his behaviour are a process in which change is constantly occurring. We can modify our behaviour in ways of our choosing.'[6] People, we are told, are not born, fated to follow one path or another. In this respect, these therapies suggest they have a radically new way of viewing the mind. Instead of seeing the personality as something fixed from the beginning, either by our genes, or by our immediate environment and history, these therapies view personality as always able to change. Ortega, we are told approvingly in a book on transactional analysis, defines man as 'a being which consists not so much of what it is as what it is going to be.'[7] People then are viewed as fluid, theoretically free, in a process of becoming.

In fact, closer examination shows these ideas are much less novel than might first appear. It has to be said immediately that this idea of the person as process is *not* an idea of a person in perpetual process, whose identity is never fixed. The fact that changes can be made is not supposed to indicate that the person will always be fluid, changeable, and unpredictable. Instead, this notion of fluidity is about *becoming* in the sense of realizing a potential or essence, which already exists but has been denied: 'this process can free us and allow us to be fully responsive enabling us to explore the expanded potential which is within us all.'[8] Transformations are really unfoldings. It is this which explains a paradox encountered in the previous chapters. These theories of change happily co-exist with more fatalistic practices like astrology and the reason is because change, in these psychotherapies, is more often than not about becoming what you already are. Hardly surprising, therefore, to find it is the 'humanistic psychotherapies' which tend to predominate, based as they are on 'a positive view of human beings as having capacities for growth and expanding their existing potential'.[9]

The individual in these accounts is the metamorphic individual but only in so far as the metamorphosis will be into what he or she ought to have become, had circumstances been different,

the metamorphic practitioner acts as a catalyst and the energy, the power of life within the recipient, takes over and does the work of transformation, of metamorphosis from one who is to one who can be. A light touch is used on the spinal reflexes in the feet, hands and head which correspond to the time before birth when we established our characteristics.[10]

The Metamorphic Association then goes on to give a clear indication of how so many of these therapies are viewed: 'many people use this technique every week as a tool for growth and realization of their potential.'[11] In this respect, change is something of a misnomer. Adjustment would be more accurate, and adjustment to allow expression to what has previously been denied. 'Adjustment is an ongoing, creative process of being and becoming. The development of our awareness is the process through which we discover who we are and what we wish to become.'[12]

'Awareness' is a term which occurs over and over again. Frequently changing is not about something radically new but about 'becoming aware', coming to know yourself and your potential. It is obvious that these ideas derive from, or at least relate extremely closely to, the 'growth' movement which established itself in the 1970s. These are the philosophies which conjure up visions of encounter groups, and growth centres, places where you can 'go and be encouraged to meet other people *and yourself* [my emphasis] in an atmosphere which enables you to open up and trust the situation enough so you can leap forward in self-understanding and human relationships'.[13] The difference at the moment is that these ideas have converged significantly with ideas of health and illness. Meeting yourself, your real self, that is, has become synonymous with meeting the possibility of health. As The Venerable Lama Sogyal Rinpoche told the Festival of Mind, Body and Spirit, 'We all have the potential within us to become enlightened, to heal, to overcome our difficulties.'

In fact, disease and long term ailments, especially those which conventional medicine have been unable to eradicate, have been taken up by these movements as fuel to fire the need for personal change. Appropriating the language of the alternative therapies movement which insists on dis-ease as a sign of fundamental problems in ourselves, these psychotherapies offer themselves as the 'solution' to calls to make personal changes. In the arena of the health movement, illness or personal disturbance is the clarion call for change and as such must no longer be dreaded. These symptoms are a call for help, a sign that the body or spirit wants changes. Similarly the psychotherapies movement has turned to disease as a sign from the person that changes must be made in attitude, behaviour and consciousness. After a crisis there is a 'chance to re-examine all aspects of ourselves with a view to change and unfoldment, thus preventing a recurrence of the crisis. This involves re-assessing our motivation, sense of purpose and meaning in life and our capabilities.'[14]

Even something which is intensely painful must be regarded as a positive sign since 'the pain of frustration is necessary for change'.[15] So strong is the sense that disease, crisis or illness is integral to your fundamental being that in many of these therapies there is an idea that illness can become a friend. No longer something to be cut out, irradiated and obliterated, disease can be welcomed as a messenger, 'in time the symptom which one had painfully endured, feared or hated before, will have a chance to become the force which induces change, personal growth and a greater degree of wholeness.'[16] One book tell us to Love Our Disease, to treat it gently and with acceptance. Not only has the disease been doing something for us but it can become the motivating force to the changes that will save us, 'In dealing with an area of consciousness where we have a block we need to first experience . . . the emotion we have locked up in that area in a loving, accepting way.'[17]

Disease then has become the motor for widespread individual and collective change, change which, in some versions has epochal significance. The threat of illness and the promise of true health are the stick and the carrot by which individuals will turn to therapies which will help them change. The changes people will be forced to make will ultimately transform all of humanity, making this the dawn of a new age. 'Humanity is on the verge of a major evolutionary step which can be achieved through a change in consciousness.'[18] But what exactly is it that, in terms of attitudes and emotions, is causing the problems? Even if it is a case of excavating already-existing potentials, what is the state of consciousness that will produce the well person? And how should we achieve it?

Clearing and past pain

In spite of the differences in techniques, there is a shared metaphor in the ideas around finding well-being through changing consciousness. It is the metaphor of clearing blockages. It is difficult to avoid some variant of the metaphor. We are going to look, one seminar promises, 'at what is blocking us to be in touch with our self-healing potential'.[19] A similar project comes from another work-shop, this time on Personal Empowerment, 'What stops you from expressing in your inner life more of who you really are? . . . In this workshop you will free up self-imposed limitations, uncover-ing your inner power to be a creator of the best and highest in our world.'[20]

Clearing, freeing, melting, dissolving or releasing from block-ages; this is the main work of the consciousness industries. Leonard Orr, guru of Rebirthing, tells us how we can use a certain book 'as a clearing process'.[21] Joanna Noble, lecturing on 'Women's Spirituality in the New Age', tells us how women 'have to look at the pain that has been put upon them and put it aside'. We will not feel better, we are told, 'until we tackle the physical compression (tension) in our body and begin to feel lighter again'.[22] Creative Visualisation suggests we can 'discover ways in which we have been holding ourselves back, blocking ourselves from achieving satisfaction and fulfilment in life through fears and negative concepts.'[23] Sound Therapy shows how 'sound can release distress and transform our consciousness',[24] whereas the British Rebirth Society can assist 'the process of dissolving the tensions permanently'.[25]

These blockages invariably come from our past. They are 'the thoughts based on fear, sadness, anxiety or frustration, from the past, usually early childhood.'[26] There is an extraordinarily strong impression which emerges across all these therapies: our personal histories are riddled with pain, distress and trauma, blocking us from achieving our full capacities.

> Human infants have remarkable though undeveloped capacities for love, understanding and choice . . . but they are highly vulnerable to interference by others – the blocking, frustration, rejection, or neglect of their deep human potential. The result of such interference is a line of distress in the mind-body, the emotional pain of grief, fear, anger, shame and embarrassment, together with correlated physical, often muscular, tension.[27]

Never has there been a time in history when people have rep-resented themselves as so damaged – riven with anger, aggression, frustrated ambition, unfulfilled needs. Never has there been a time when people thought of themselves so strongly as victims or prisoners to our past.

Most of the therapies have slightly different explanations for the source of pain. For some it is contact with other 'toxic people'; for others it is bad parenting; others prioritize the 'birth trauma'; and yet others attribute human deprivation to the general lack of attention to spiritual well-being. But for most there is a prevalent belief that we live in 'an emotionally repressive society' which has first of all invalidated what we are and then invalidated the pain and frustration we feel at this denial. So dire is the scenario of our past pains that we are exhorted quite literally to start again – to be reborn (in rebirthing therapy), to be 'reparented' (in transactional analysis), or to 'change our personal history' (as in neuro-linguistic processing). The scenarios of past damage are rarely rooted in specific history, and even more rarely offer material explanations as to *why* families and groups of people have interacted in the way that is said to have damaged us. Instead the focus is on discharging the pain, on letting the pain and anger be heard so that it can be truly externalized and 'let go'. *Cutting the Ties that Bind* is both an enormously popular book and a prevalent metaphor. There is an all-pervasive sense that the past must be left behind.[28]

The connotations which attach to these 'blockages' from the past are extremely negative; they are 'the toxic power of the past', which one book on Gestalt therapy offers to 'melt'.[29] They are our own 'deep-seated negative concepts about life',[30] the result of 'accumulating negative mental mass'.[31] It is, as an adherent to the Networking Movement announced, just like eradicating junk food from our diet. 'We should do the same for the mind . . . We have to feed ourselves and others spiritually.'[32] The past in all these accounts is just so much rubbish, junk, clutter. Our minds, we are told, are like the refuse dumps of an affluent society. They house mental attitudes which should not be there, which are holding us back, and causing us pain. There is nothing clear and productive about these emotions. They are wasteful and dark, inhibitions to ourselves.

In many of these beliefs, there is a rather hazy notion of the 'subconscious' or unconscious, hanging on to these negative forces and preventing us from realizing our true potential, or as one of the self-appointed gurus of self-empowerment puts it, 'the subconscious is all that stands between you now and your beautiful self.'[33] Thus most of the therapies are designed to persuade this bit of ourselves to give up. There are a number of preferred ways in which these therapies set about clearing the blockages. Blocks, we are told, are caused 'by repressed emotions of fear, guilt and/or resentment/ anger which cause a person to tighten up and close down spiritually, emotionally, mentally and even physically'.[34] It is therefore common to find that the first stage in 'clearing' is to try and make a patient 'aware' of these blocks: 'we need first to experience . . . the emotion we have locked up in that area.' 'Awareness' is usually seen as the first step to healing if the struggle against being conscious of these negative thoughts and feelings is what has made her or him ill.

> When the individual perceives that consciousness itself does him no harm but rather shows him the harm he does to himself, he relaxes and his organism immediately ceases to liberate the hormones responsible for his tension and stress. From this point to the cure the path is short and direct; and the organism itself and its immune and homeostatic system takes charge of eliminating all types of illness.[35]

Not all the therapists insist on direct awareness of past emotions. There are a number of other strategies offered for dealing with our blockages. One is hypnosis, where suggestions are made to the subconscious mind to give up its hindrances. In hypnosis, the subconscious mind is simply outwitted. In a state of deep relaxation, the individual is persuaded that she doesn't really think what she thinks. Another strategy is offered by neuro-linguistic processing which teaches us how to find new mental responses or processes so we give up the 'junk' of our habitual responses. One 'textbook' tells how neuro-linguistic processing cured a woman's fear of heights. When the therapist discovered she always imagined the feeling of falling which then made her feel physically sick, he taught her to approach heights singing the national anthem instead! This, the book claimed, did the trick, preventing her habitual patterns of response.[36] In these kinds of treatment the past memories, emotions and their causes don't have to become conscious. The idea is that the mind is just persuaded to give them up and become clear to respond to immediate circumstances without clutter from the past.

Whether or not conscious awareness of what caused the blockages is necessary, the psychotherapies in vogue around natural therapies have more points of similarity than difference. Each believes in the very profound damage done to us by our past; each believes fundamentally in the possibility and necessity of change; each believes that subconscious or unconscious feelings can be left behind or tricked; and each holds out the lure of becoming well, healed, a whole person or 'clear'. It is difficult not to notice some of the more curious imagery that attaches to these ideas. Taken *en masse*, there are inescapable connotations of a war against toxic accumulation and waste. Blocks being 'where energy is constricted, not moving, not flowing',[37] their removal is a bit like a cure for a sort of mental constipation. The metaphors for removing these blockages are strangely chemical; the outcome oddly hygienic. It is as if whole areas of human emotion have to be purged and the human being left clear. There are vague resonances with Scientology's vision of the 'clears', people who have been able to clear away all negative clutter from the past and past lives. These rather odd connotations suggest that we need to understand something more about the goals pursued by these healing therapies and the techniques by which the so-called revolution in consciousness can be accomplished.

Self-fulfilment and its material advantages

Explicitly, at least, clearing is about becoming whole, finding a sense of wholeness in yourself which will also be synonymous with physical well-being, hence the endless proliferation of centres of 'holistic psychotherapy'. But becoming a whole person is a pretty elastic concept. As soon as you begin to look a little more closely at what is actually on offer, what begins to emerge is a rather odd combination of goals. At one moment the cleared person looks like a peaceful yogi, quietly meditating and getting in touch with his or her higher self. At another moment, there are distinct and unavoidable implications that the route of clearing is a route to material self-advancement whose objectives take in just about anything from becoming rich to getting the ideal body.

At first sight questions about what exactly the goals of trans-forming consciousness are may seem a little displaced. Most people are driven to both mind and body therapies through disabling symptoms, either mental problems like phobias or anxieties, or physical illnesses, usually those which conventional medicine has turned its back on. Most of the therapies which offer specifically to deal with transformations of the mind and emotions focus on eradicating 'deep-seated negative concepts' or shifting disabling forms of behaviour. Most commonly the therapies offer themselves as being able to deal with phobias, anxieties, health-damaging habits, allergies, and with various physical ailments. Advertise-ments for therapies or natural health centres more often than not look like this one: 'Acupuncture, Reflexology, Counselling, Shiatsu, Therapeutic Massage etc. . . . to improve stress-related conditions, physical conditions, apathy, depression, tiredness . . . and to help restore physical and mental well-being.'[38]

Given this, surely any process which tackles and shifts these problems let alone clears them away, is a justifiable end in itself? This may be so. But it is also undeniably the case that a whole lot more is on offer to the client. It is rare to meet one of these 'healing' therapies which suspends assumptions about the expected out-come. At the very least, most make nebulous offers of personal growth with accompanying increases in energy, well-being and satisfaction from life, promises embodied in the claim of Reiki therapy to 'reduce tension and stress, expand creativity and productivity, renew and revitalize your energy, support personal growth and transformation, enhance the quality of your life'.[39] It would be extremely unusual to encounter such a pessimistic (or realistic?) promise as that made by Freud who claimed that the most psychoanalysis could offer was to convert disabling neurosis into everyday misery. No, in today's consciousness industries, we have some very specific objectives; almost all of these attempts to transform consciousness entertain definite assumptions about appropriate emotions and objectives for a well, or healed, person.

On the surface there appear to be two distinctive sets of objectives promised by the consciousness therapies. On the one hand, there's the objective of the whole person or self-fulfilled person. This person is the one who will find a natural potential within her- or him-self. There's a distinct suggestion that this whole person, the person in harmony with the natural forces of health, will also be in touch with the harmony of the universe. On the other hand there's the quest for the 'self-realized' person, happy with their own desires and determined to fulfil those desires. In fact it is quite difficult to maintain an absolute distinction between these two sets of objectives.

Looking at the apparent split between specific material objectives and the more philosophical or religious quest for the whole person, it could easily be said that this simply reflects the difference between the 'authentic' therapies and the appropriation of these therapies into exploitative, self-help, how-to manuals. There's an element of truth in this but only an element. The distinction between the idea of an authentic, non-exploitative therapy and the commercial, materialistic therapies is often hard to maintain since the well person is very often the person able to achieve her desires, ambitions and fulfil herself in directly materialistic ways. The titles on the 'self-help' shelves give the game away, *The Wealth Within* by Ainslie Meares, or *Getting What You Want* by J. H. Brennan, *Choose Happiness* by Elizabeth Smith, and Napoleon Hill's and Clement W. Stone's *Success through a Positive Mental Attitude*. Or as a self-management programme put it, there can be very great gains from 'exploring the relationship between body, mind, emotions, and spirit thereby increasing self-awareness and clarifying aims and goals on the journey of life'.[40]

Even the apparently simple aim of being aware has a sort of material outcome. Becoming aware is not just about becoming aware of your past, and the blockages and problems created by past traumas. Becoming aware is also a goal in itself, a state of heightened consciousness in which reality is experienced in a spontaneous, uninhibited, pleasureable way. Heightened awareness becomes a way not just of getting rid of fears and anxieties but also of having more, of having a better quality of experience. Thus there is even pre-birth counselling on offer, where parents can deal with and clear their inhibitions, problems and blockages around birth so that they can have a heightened experience. Similarly, the International Centre for Active Birth 'provides a context in which parents-to-be can explore alternatives, increase self-awareness and understanding in order to have the best possible experience of pregnancy, labour and birth'.[41] The movement is shot through with these acquisitive implications. Make changes and you can have more and better. There is nothing you cannot have and you can have the best.

At the most general level, personal growth is theorized in terms of liberating creative potential and personal strength which have been blocked from expression, 'the discovery in ourselves of hidden powers'. But as soon as it comes to specifying what exactly is meant by this deepening of self-understanding and expanding vital capacities, more definite goals and objectives emerge. For many of the therapies, these definite objectives are religious. The aim is to free the 'higher' part of ourselves which is able to be in touch with universals. Thus meditation, which is regularly suggested as a vital component of transforming therapies, is seen as getting 'in tune with your higher self'.[42] Consciousness in these approaches is actually about a consciousness of some connection of the individual mind with other humans; higher consciousness is about discovering what is common to all humans, universals like peace, joy, and inner harmony: 'To descend consciously into that pristine state of yourself while still alive – to realize it without the possibility of ever being separate from it again – is the unconscious motivation of all human endeavour.' Or at least that's what Barry Long[43] thinks.

The voices of such self-appointed gurus are not isolated. These psychotherapies are full of such assumptions; they are returning to people that sense of the spiritual to be achieved by 'conscious awareness' of their spiritual capacities. 'Humanistic psychotherapy' has increasingly come to include in its self-definition 'the more spiritual aspects of psychology' and is happy to include 'transpersonal psychotherapy' under its umbrella. Indeed there is a widespread push towards transpersonal psychotherapy which acknowledges, includes or aims for those 'peak experiences when we seem to be in touch with the whole universe'. This is undoubtedly one of the main reasons for the extraordinary growth in sympathy for Jung and Jungian-based psychotherapy, which has 'not only underlined the importance of unconscious factors, both individual and collective, in the human growth process but [has] shown how individuals can become whole, and fulfil all sides of their nature'.[44] Including and especially the spiritual side.

The little graphics which attach themselves to the various

counselling and therapy centres tend to give the ideology away before one even looks at the texts. Little 'symbols', pentagrams, moons, the symbols of yin and yang, circles with spiralling symbols inside, all attempt to convey a philosophy which is in touch with the 'mysteries' of life that have been revealed by oriental philosophies and religions. The ideology of such symbols is pretty clear. They stress balance, equivalence, symmetry. The world in this ideology is not a world of conflict and struggle but of order and peace. The self-fulfilled person in this account is the one who has cleared all the past junk sufficiently and has therefore been able to find these universals in his or her own mind. There might appear to be a paradox in these particular views of consciousness. They appear to stress the importance of 'conscious awareness', heightened experience, but at the same time imply that higher experiences involve loss of a sense of self and a feeling of contact with universal emotions, like peace, harmony and joy.

In fact it is not so much a paradox as might appear. For one thing, these transformations of the consciousness are far from threatening to a sense of individuality. It is just that they insist that the *real* self, or higher self, contains these definite, nameable universal attributes. The other crucial factor is that these apparently self-negating aspirations are, as I have already begun to suggest, strangely rooted in self-realization in the material world. There is a fortuitous to and fro between realization of the higher self, and self-realization in material terms. To find your higher self is very often offered as a way of freeing the blockages to self-realization in the more mundane world; to 'become conscious' is also to become more effective in the real world. 'Most people in our culture have become cut off from their awareness of who they really are . . . they have temporarily lost their conscious connection with their higher selves and thus lost their sense of power and responsibility for their lives.'[45]

Many of the therapies do not even have to deal with this apparent paradox. More often than not, the process of self-discovery is about being able to discover what it is that we really want and to fulfil these desires. One psychology self-help book presents itself as revealing the 'secret of bridging the gap between what you have now and what you desire'. Owning up to these needs is the first step to transformation. 'Taking responsibility for ourselves means responding to our own needs'[46] and this, we are told, is the true meaning of 'response-ability'. The author goes on to explain what the goals of this new self-understanding would be, 'to relax, stop worrying, be more assertive, feel less anxious'. Again and again we encounter very definite goals of consciousness, 'feeling more comfortable, relaxed and accepting of self-worth'.[47] The goals set are: self-acceptance, self-valuation, self-fulfilment and living comfortably with one's desires. We can use our imaginations to get 'what we want in life . . . love, fulfilment, enjoyment, satisfying relationships, rewarding work, self-expression, health, beauty, prosperity, inner peace and harmony.'[48]

It is in this area of our 'real wants' or 'needs' that the whole confusion around the material promises of these therapies arises. When pushed, most adherents of these therapies define human potential as the capacity for joy, love and fulfilment which sounds pretty anti-materialistic, if rather vague. Yet self-fulfilment for many of the therapies often means overcoming inhibitions to success, which in turn suggests material advancement in the world, whether it be through actually earning more money, getting a permanent relationship, or losing weight. Creative visualization, for example, can only ever be used for good, 'as a means of unblocking or dissolving the barriers we ourselves have created to the naturally harmonious, abundant and loving flow of the universe'. Yet once unblocked, the way is happily open to becoming a social (and sexual) success, 'the more I love and appreciate myself, the more beautiful I am becoming. I am now irresistibly attractive to men (or women).'[49] The whole of assertiveness training is based precisely on a philosophy that our own internalized inhibitions are standing in the way of self-expression, getting what we want, and very often this means material success.

Practitioners of established therapies might be 'sniffy' about the endless self-help manuals that they have spawned but the fact is that there is no clear line between using these skills for self-advancement or to discover inner peace. Indeed for many of the therapies the division is a false one. Material successes are merely ways of realizing our creative potential. Feeling guilty or inhibited about being effective in the world is just more of the junk from our past. But the vision of the person who has grown and found self-fulfilment is often a depressingly ideological vision of someone who accepts and fits in with the oppressive values of Western society. Thus there is, for example, sometimes a complete acceptance that women would do anything for a traditional relationship with a man. In *How to Make a Man Fall in Love with You* Tracy Cabot suggests using the techniques of neuro-linguistic processing to ensure a man falls for you, remains entranced by you and settles down into a permanent relationship with you. She suggests using the techniques of understanding *how* a person thinks, to 'mirror' their processes, making them feel comfortable and understood. Thus we are told to watch the potential victim's eye movements when you ask him if he wants steak for dinner, 'If he looks up to his "past" visual side you'll be fairly sure he's having a visual memory about steak from his past. You might say, "Are you remembering another wonderful meal?" If he looks to his future visual side, you might ask, 'What kind of dinner do you see us having?" ' Whichever way, he'll be hooked, 'He'll be so amazed that you can read his mind.'

The ideology in Tracy Cabot's seduction scenario is pretty clear, even down to the frilly undies and tight jeans suggested to satisfy the 'visual man'. Women need completion with a permanent partner and anything is worth doing to get him. Masculine behaviour is to be accepted unproblematically; the task of the seeking woman is to mirror the man's desires. The ideology in other areas of human behaviour is much more subtle and hidden but no less present for that. Take attitudes towards self-advancement and career. The process of Rebeliefing for example not only offers 'freedom from all mental stress and freedom from all psychological problems'. You can also be reprogrammed to 'achieve your life-long amibitions'. The goal of this process will be the 'achiever status'. In fact, during the rebeliefing process 'applicants will move through the various stages towards becoming a Total Achiever.' These are 'confident, optimistic people. They can talk to anyone, command attention and are winners.' Indeed such are their phenomenal attributes that Total Achievers 'often look many years younger than they really are' because with 'rebeliefing it is possible to slow down the ageing process as you erase the old beliefs, relieve all mental stress and overcome problems'.[50]

What this rather extreme example foregrounds is the characteristic promise of therapy to help you 'effortlessly achieve your goals' and the power attributed to the mind in accomplishing real changes in the external world. This overlap between internal transformations and external achievements can be seen quite clearly in the rather curious attitude to money in these popular psychotherapies. At one end there's the extremely hazy area of concerns which hides under the concept of 'abundance' much favoured by some of the consciousness-transforming therapies. 'Abundance' as a concept is meant to signal a whole attitude to life, and humanistic psychology proudly proclaims itself to be 'abundance-orientated'. Experiencing life as abundant and oneself as well supplied is one of the much-vaunted offers of mental transformation. The aim of this mental transformation is the destruction of emotions like envy. But there's a very odd way in which this destruction shades into creating a new attitude towards money which is going to be rewarding. Thus we are offered 'programmes' on 'money' where the aim is to make sure that 'money will no longer be a problem in your life. We will work on both the external and practical aspects of making money and managing it as well as your internal relationships with money which determines your money situation.'[51]

It is hardly surprising to discover such attitudes happily coexisting with quite blatant suggestions that if you change your attitude you can get rich. This is spelled out in the book, *Money is My Friend*, where a rebirther, Philip Laut 'describes techniques that have increased the incomes of thousands of people in all walks of life'. In his account, since 'all wealth is created by the human mind', it is a simple matter of doing 'exercises to increase self-esteem', thereby 'demolishing the poverty consciousness'. This book is one amongst many. Numerous others, like *Getting What You Want*, *Getting Rich*, *The Prosperity Secrets of the Age* and *23 Steps to Success and Achievement* similarly promise more money will follow from changing your attitude. In these accounts there is no objective reality to poverty and hardship. There is no sense of the structural and cultural inequalities between various groups. Getting rich is simply a matter of having the right attitude, of 'unleashing the colossal forces in your mind' which will drive you forward to greater prosperity.[52]

It is hardly surprising then that so many of these psychotherapies occupy a curious between-land, shared by alternative therapies on the one hand, and business skills and management training courses on the other. Some of the therapies make no secret about their usefulness to management training and marketing. The skills they can release are connected with realizing ambition, with being able to set goals and objectives and carry them through. They promise self-confidence and self-assertion, an ability to influence people with these qualities. Sometimes there's an offer to understand other people and how they arrive at decisions, all of which is highly useful for marketing and business. Many of the therapies and their techniques are used, regardless of whether many practitioners would approve, in manuals and courses specifically and overtly concerned with personal advancement in material terms. The transformation of consciousness is more than just a tool to deal with personal distress; it is also an industry teaching success in a highly competitive and oppressive society.

The power of positive thought

Probably the single most important factor in the consciousness industries is the assertion of the importance of individual attitude and individual emotional state both in determining self-limits and in determining new possibilities. Throughout all the literature – whether it be to do with healing physical ailments, achieving work goals or more religious aspirations – there's a consistent assertion. A changed set of attitudes can change one's entire life. 'Poverty transformed into riches . . . loneliness into love . . . disgrace into glory . . . failure into success . . . all by using The Magical Powers of Self-Image Psychology.'[53] Not only is there the assumption that we can and should change, but there is an insistence that the crucial factor in determining overall change is the mind and our attitude towards ourselves. This becomes crystal clear when you look at the techniques which are prevalent as the means to accomplish mental transformations.

Regardless of different material aims, there are some significant shared techniques of mental change, in particular techniques concerned with the power of thought to transform existing situations. This is evidenced in the widespread belief in the power of 'setting goals'. Lurking in many of these popular psychotherapies is an idea that self-fulfilment will only be possible when we have a clear picture of our own goals and objectives. The processes by which these goals are to be uncovered or given expression differ from therapy to therapy. For some, the process of discovering the goals is the process of therapy itself. In these, the client's journey of self-exploration will be a journey of clearing the blockages and inhibitions which stand in the way of understanding what our goals would be.

In other therapies less concerned with unconscious blockages, the process of therapy is a matter of setting realistic goals and finding ways of pursuing these goals unencumbered by the hinderances of past negative mental mass. Whatever the process, and regardless of whether or not the therapy specifies in concrete terms what exactly your goals are, there are shared assumptions that your real self can be found, and that this real self will have definite goals. In many of the therapies, regardless of how these goals have been recognized, there is a strong belief that once the goals are known, they can in themselves operate as 'a carrot', persuading either the body or the emotions to fall into line: 'people who are successful in life usually have some kind of representation inside their head . . . [which] acts very much like a carrot in front of a donkey, tempting, enticing, encouraging the person . . . forward.'[54]

Nowhere can these assumptions be seen more clearly at work than in the widespread commitment to 'positive visualization' as a route to healing. The idea of visualization crops up all over the place – as an element in meditation, as the separate technique of creative visualization, as 'guided imagery' in hypnosis and deep relaxation techniques. In all of these, visualization involves the formation of 'positive' imagery – either of something we would like to be or something we would like to happen. These images are most effective, we are told, in a state of deep relaxation when they can insert themselves in our subconscious and become part of our being, chasing away the shadows of negative and limiting self-definitions. As with all these therapies, there is a range covering anything and everything between the sublime and the ridiculous. On the one hand, visualization techniques are used to 'Think Yourself Thin' in the late 1970s' answer to the crash diet. On the other, they are used, apparently with enormous success, at places like the Bristol Cancer Centre as a way of imagining the body restoring itself to health.

'Visualization' as a fundamental element in helping us accomplish our desires, whether for weight loss or health, implies that the mind can have absolute control over matter, albeit indirectly. In spite of the fact that there are many references to the subconscious or the unconscious, there is a clear sense that in fact ultimately our consciousness is in the driving seat *and* that we are in control of this aspect of our mind. It is as if the mind were made up of parts, but one part – our conscious intention – is ultimately in control. The implication is clear. If thought has the power to restrict us, inhibit us, and make us ill, then 'positive' thought has the ability to restore us, 'healing through consciousness' as the title of one book makes perfectly clear. Thought in these theories becomes a source of energy in itself, perhaps the most potent source of energy there is, able even to influence external reality; 'in creative visualization you use your imagination to create a clear image of something you wish to manifest. Then you continue to focus on the idea or picture regularly, giving it positive energy until it becomes objective reality.'[55]

The power of visualization is often accomplished by another force for instilling positive thoughts to clear away past negativity, that is, the power of affirmation. If we can only teach ourselves how to make positive affirmations about ourselves and our lives, they will ultimately become the reality of our lives. 'The concepts we hold of ourselves determine our health and beauty or the lack thereof. When we change our concepts, our physical self follows suit.'[56] As with all this area of self-transformation, there is an extremely hazy area about what these affirmations are good for. We can either use them to get in touch with the 'healthy', loving, creative, harmonious self assumed to be our higher self. Or we can use them to free the self for greater self-advancement, to make ourselves beautiful, rich and successful.

There is something rather offensive about the convergence of Eastern spirituality and Western materialism in the suggested affirmations for accepting oneself. 'It is okay for me to have fun and enjoy myself and I do! I like to do things that make me feel good. I am always deeply relaxed and centred. I now feel deep inner peace and serenity. I'm glad I was born and I love being alive.'[57] It may well be that this path is in the service of good, and that negative self concepts are extremely damaging to self and others. However, there is an unmistakable odour of Californian self-absorption and self-advancement which attaches to these ideas. The social implication is that there is no reason why we shouldn't have everything we want. All our needs and desires are all right and just need to be validated. We have to stop feeling guilty about what we want and make it happen for ourselves. At no point is there any discussion of the *conflict* of interests and needs which may exist between two individuals, for example between a man who might want sado-masochistic sex and a woman who doesn't. There's an implicit promise that somehow these therapeutic practices will make us nice, nourishing and considerate, but it's hard to see exactly how if individuals are being encouraged to fulfil all their desires in a society built on inequality.

In all these theories the aim of transformation is to restore to the individual a sense of power: 'You can improve or control the quality of your thoughts.' It involves the individual in 'taking responsibility for the quality of your thoughts . . . [and] dissolving the lies that you have brought from other people throughout your life.'[58] The power of the conscious mind is all-important in these ideas of self-transformation. Indeed so important is it that claims are frequently made that changes in individual consciousness will in fact alter external society. These claims go considerably further than claims that large-scale personal changes can amount to major social transformations. Instead these theories border on the megalomaniac. Individual thought, we are told, has an objective power; it can even change external reality. For example, we are invited to join 'a very special meditation'. Its aim is 'to bring about world peace by generating positive spiritual energy constructively channelled, for peace, love, harmony, and healing, which will make the suburb of Epping into a "world centre for Peace, Love, Harmony and Healing." ' 'By each person who joins us "switching on" positively . . . so will more and more "lights" go on all over the world . . . People are being asked to give just one minute (any minute) for the visualization, on the basis that by so doing we shall collectively reach a point eventually when someone, somewhere is visualizing Epping as a World Centre for Peace, Love, Harmony and Healing, every minute of every day.'[59]

This is undoubtedly a benign, if eccentric, view of the power of positive thought. Other implications of the power of positive thought are considerably less appetizing. We have already seen how there is a strongly materialistic and acquisitive streak to these ideas of self-fulfilment and self-transformation. But far more objectionable is the implication that our attitude is ultimately responsible for everything which happens to us. By a sleight of hand the reality of hardship and of living in a society based on divisions of sex, race and class are obliterated. All hardships are seen as the result of negative thinking. All success and well-being is seen as the result of a positive mental attitude, as in 'All wealth is created by the human mind.'[60] Such ideas might have resonances for individuals who have been raised in an affluent Western society and have never known hardship. Transposed to the third world, such a suggestion is laughable if not offensive. Even within our own culture, the ideas are pretty unacceptable, since they suggest that an individual is to blame for his or her own hardships when in fact we live in a society in which certain individuals have power and advantages at the expense of other groups.

Let us give these ideas the benefit of the doubt. Let us assume that such materialistic and conservative versions of the power of positive thinking are atypical. For many of the adherents the great attraction of these psychotherapies is not that they promise personal advancement or that they are a condemnation of those in distress. Instead the attraction is that they have restored power and responsiblity to the individual mind which previous psychological theories had denied. They have revealed the power of the mind to work for ill and good. They claim that psychoanalysis is too deterministic, not allowing the individual ever to be cured, or ever to be free of unconscious thoughts. On the other hand they pronounce themselves as hostile to behaviourism, which assumes that what matters above anything are the forms of behaviour which an individual exhibits. Thus behaviourist 'therapy' tends to consist in trying to alter the behaviour so that the individual no longer exhibits the worrying symptoms.

Yet it is very difficult for me to accept the absolute distinctions which these 'new' therapies draw between themselves and behaviourism. In positing the absolute interconnections between consciousness, body and emotions, these theories seem to have come up with just a slightly different, sometimes inverted, version of behaviourism. Behaviour and emotions can be brought into line with mind and aspirations, rather than mind brought into line with alterations of behaviour. But the model of the interrelation between mind and behaviour has distinct similarities. Both rely on the possibility of a simple and direct correspondence between mind and behaviour. 'Negative' concepts always produce negative (self-defeating) behaviour; 'positive' concepts always produce creative (self-fulfilling) behaviour. There is no real sense in either of these approaches that one's will, intention, mind and body very often cannot be brought into a neat line with one another, that unconscious intentions might be as important as behaviour patterns or conscious intentions.

What is, in fact, implicit in most of the therapies which insist on the necessity and ease of personal transformation is that everything is conscious (which is ultimately the same assumption that behaviourism makes). In spite of gestures to the idea of the unconscious, most of these theories assume that we can get our mind under control and make it do what we want. Ideas of goal setting, positive affirmation and positive self-image all ultimately deny the existence of the unconscious. Instead they insist that the individual conscious mind is truly in charge of our destiny. Therapy becomes a matter of making contact with that conscious self and making it work. And with that aim, change becomes a matter of will-power. Yet all the evidence is that the relation between mind, body and emotions is much more complex. Psychoanalysis and psychoanalytical-derived therapy are infinitely more sympathetic to the fact that our own behaviour is never fully under our conscious control, that the very best of intentions are liable to subversion from unconscious desires and needs formed in our past history.

Conclusions

On the surface these therapies of self-transformation appear to offer a version of the person which is not irreversibly determined by any force external to itself, like God or the Devil, as Christianity might suggest, or bourgeois society, as a theory like Marxism holds. Instead there is a triumphant restoration of power to the individual, who is no longer victim to these external forces but able to transform her or his self purely through the power of her own mind. Many claim the theories 'free human potential' perhaps for the first time in Western history. But there is no escaping the fact that any theory which relies on the all-importance of human will-power is ultimately committed to distinctly conservative views of society. Adherents might think their ideas are centrally about freeing individuals from the negative pull of the past and allowing the possibility of healing. However, the centrality attributed to the conscious mind and will-power, can only be fodder for conservative views of the world with their insistence that advantages are the reward of talent and hardship is the punishment of weakness.

These notions of the personality and the power attributed to the individual will are hardly new to Western society. In spite of the whole emphasis on change and transformation, these therapies carry, no less than all previous Western religions, assumptions about the innate essence of the human individual, and the responsibility of the individual for determining whether life is hard or easy. And no less than with previous views of consciousness, there is an implicit morality. All across the board the lure of these therapies is the calm, self-accepting individual who is in some way in harmony with him- or herself and her environment. The whole person is not the self-denying, good, moral person of Christianity. Indeed the route to becoming whole often involves learning to accept those areas of human behaviour so frowned on by religion. But he or she is 'centred', 'nourishing', self-valuing and self-fulfilled. And most importantly he or she is, as with Christianity, very much responsible for his or her fate. It is within the power of the individual to determine their own life. Indeed the ideas have gone much further. Not only must individuals take responsibility for their own lives; these transformations can now alter even external reality.

Almost all these psychotherapies would claim not to be judgmental about a person, and to occupy a totally different space from those views of Western religion which saw people or behaviour as intrinsically good or bad. In these new accounts, there is nothing to suggest that people are 'evil', 'degraded' or 'corrupt'. Anyone and any kind of behaviour can be accepted and validated. Indeed, a vital part of the process of change in most of these therapies is recognizing and owning up to those areas of our personality which a repressive religion and society have made us feel bad about. Yet ideas of good and evil still abound. The role of therapy is to save the personality from distortions and corruptions and to restore what is, after all, some version of original good, that is an original potential for creativity and inner harmony.

There is a paradox here. Many of these therapies seem eager to embrace what have traditionally been viewed as 'bad' aspects of the person – rage, aggression, avarice, competitiveness, envy and hate. Indeed the seven deadly sins would not seem out of place among some of the emotions described. But to say that they were truly accepted would be a grave misrepresentation. These emotions are no more finally sanctioned than they were in religion. They are accepted in the way one might warmly embrace a departing guest. For they are seen by the therapies as ultimately negative and self-destructive. 'The first step to healing is to conscientize the emotions of envy, fear and anger. The second step is to perceive the reasons for such attitudes and the fact that they belong to the realms of will; that is, envy, anger, and fear are attitudes, they are reactions which we may or may not adopt in the face of consciousness.'[61] These emotions won't exactly send us to hell but they will make our life a misery. And the aim of transforming our consciousnesses is to clear us of these emotions.

There's a tension which runs through all these fashionable therapies for self-transformation. Are they exclusively concerned with states of inner harmony, balance and well-being? Or will they make us more effective citizens in a society based on inequality? There is no easy answer to these questions. Most of the therapies contain elements of both. Sometimes wholeness, inner harmony and well-being shade effortlessly into material success and self-advancement. The emphasis on the power of the individual conscious mind and will-power has provided a space for highly conservative, acquisitive and moralistic views of the individual to flourish. The call from within the health movement for us to transform ourselves in order that we can become well and fight disease has been met by conservative psychotherapies. These therapies have flourished by insisting on a vision of the world, where each individual can consciously determine the outcome of her life, and where any failures can be laid at the feet of the individual.

Notes

1 *Well-Being*, Channel 4 Publications.
2 Information on Pre-Creation or Soul Therapy, Arcane Medicine Lodge.
3 Leonard Orr and Sandra Ray, *Rebirthing in the New Age*.
4 Thomas A. Harris, *I'm OK – You're OK*.
5 Richard Bandler and John Grinder, *Frogs into Princes, Neuro Linguistic Programming*.
6 Jerry Greenwald, *Be the Person You Were Meant to Be*.
7 ibid.
8 Information brochure on the Karuna Institute for Core Process Psychotherapy.
9 John Rowan, *A Guide to Humanistic Psychology*.
10 Information brochure of the Metamorphic Association.
11 ibid.
12 Greenwald, op. cit.
13 Rowan, op. cit.
14 Centre for Counselling and Psychotherapy Education brochure.
15 Greenwald, op. cit.
16 Brochure for Biodynamic therapy – Jungian and Body Work.
17 Gawain, op. cit.
18 Information on the Findhorn Foundation.
19 'Image Work and Guided Fantasy – Man and Woman'. Brochure for workshops with J. Boeneng and J. Dieffenbacher.
20 Information for workshops with the Findhorn Foundation.
21 Leonard Orr in Orr and Ray, op. cit.
22 Chiron Centre for Holistic Psychotherapy brochure.
23 Gawain, op. cit.
24 Information leaflet for 'Sound Health', London.
25 British Rebirth Society.
26 ibid.
27 'Co-counselling', in Hulke, op. cit.
28 Phyllis Krystal, *Cutting the Ties that Bind*.
29 Greenwald, op. cit.
30 Gawain, op. cit.
31 Orr and Ray, op. cit.

32 Sabine Kurjo, 'Networking in Mind, Body and Spirit', lecture at the Festival of Mind, Body and Spirit, 1987.

33 Barry Long, 'Self-Growth and the Spirit', pamphlet.

34 Gawain, op. cit.

35 Pacheco, op. cit.

36 Quoted in R. Bandler and J. Grinder, op. cit.

37 Gawain, op. cit.

38 Information brochure for the Shen/Ko Natural Therapies Centre.

39 Ray, op. cit.

40 Brunel University programme of Self-management.

41 'Active Birth Centres' in *East/West* magagine, Jan. 1987.

42 Lecture on 'Women's Spirituality', by Joanna Noble at the Festival of Mind, Body and Spirit, 1987.

43 Long, op. cit.

44 Rowan, op. cit.

45 Gawain, op. cit.

46 Greenwald, op. cit.

47 Self-management programme, Brunel University.

48 Gawain, op. cit.

49 ibid.

50 Pamphlet on Re-beliefing. Programme in Neuro-Linguistic Processing.

51 Seminars with Rosemary Kearney, advertisement in *Human Potential* magazine.

52 R. Valett, *Self-actualization: The Magical Powers of Self-Image Psychotherapy*.

53 ibid.

54 Pamphlet on Re-beliefing, op. cit.

55 Gawain, op. cit.

56 ibid.

57 ibid.

58 Orr and Ray, op. cit.

59 Brochure for World Centre for Peace, Love, Harmony and Healing, Epping.

60 Phil Laut, *Money is My Friend*.

61 Pacheco, op. cit.

5 The Meanings of Health Foods

At the heart of all these views on the importance of transforming life style lies one element of overwhelming significance – nutrition. All the advice in the healthy-living circles rests on a fundamental message – it availeth nought unless you attend to your diet. 'Healthy tissues cannot be built from deficient foods. No amount of physical exercise or the pursuit of methods of "right thinking" will yield the highest degree of health if the food eaten is unsuitable.'[1] Changing our diet in favour of healthy eating is in fact the baseline in virtually all the calls to change our lives. Here, if nowhere else, we should be able to make a definite choice in favour of health. Taking conscious decisions about what and how we eat has become the place where we can demonstrate our commitment to health and our readiness to submit to changes in pursuit of this health. In short the pursuit of a healthy diet is the principal site where we can exercise conscious control over our health. Diet is the privileged arena where the sense of personal responsibility for our health can be worked out. No wonder there has been such panic as the facts about the adulteration of food at source have become widely known.

From sex to food – the power of food

It would be extremely difficult, indeed foolish, to take issue with some of the claims made about nutrition. The evidence that various ailments characteristic of our culture such as heart disease, bowel disorders and tooth decay are linked with eating patterns seems overwhelming. Hard, too, to deny that taking a stance against some of the dominant patterns of eating in our culture reduces the incidence of these diseases. Even the British Medical Association has noted the evidence that vegetarians have 'lower rates of obesity, coronary heart disease, high blood pressure, large bowel disorders, cancer and gallstones'.[2] No one could seriously wish to challenge the evidence that the state of our bodies is directly connected with what we eat. Nevertheless there is a degree of difference between evidence and myth. And it seems clear that contemporary discussion of diet and nutrition slips frequently into mythology.

In the mythology of alternative health, food and health have become inextricably linked as if it would be impossible to be healthy without serious attention to our diet. 'Optimum nutrition is optimum health,' we are told. 'Eating healthily' has acquired meanings which link food not only to our sense of well-being, but also to the possibilities for a healthy and wholesome life. Changing our diet is offered within the alternative health movement as a sign of how serious we are about making changes. Good nutrition is seen not just as opening up new possibilities for the individual but also as a way of solving major social problems. The symbolism surrounding health foods encapsulates far more than a concern with nutrition or a critique of the social organization of food production. Instead, the symbolism links to a new sense of the inner geography of the body and the significance of this body for society in general. Nowhere are new attitudes towards health and the body clearer than in these beliefs in the power of healthy eating as a solution to all individual and social ills.

The claims made for a changed diet range from the relatively tame offer of improved vigour and energy, through 'cures' for various ailments, to the wilder promises of 'eating the "power" foods that will help you turn back the clock'.[3] Such claims should not obscure one factor of overwhelming importance. Quite simply, this is the unprecedented way in which diet has become absolutely central in any discussion of ourselves and our bodies. There is hardly a journal, magazine or newspaper which can refrain from quoting 'you are what you eat' whenever an article touches on the importance of changing your diet.

'You are what you eat.' This popular phrase has become the slogan of the nutritional seventies, reflecting our ever-increasing interest in our own good health and well-being. Through research, the scientific community is becoming more aware of how food influences our bodies and minds. New uses for known substances are being substantiated and new nutrients are being discovered.[4]

Diet and nutrition are the touchstone of any number of 'alternative' therapies. Even those not obviously connected with dietary treatment seem to recommend changes in diet, as with the Society of Homoeopaths who offer advice for 'the first steps towards a healthy diet'. Never has there been a time in history when so much energy has been invested in 'knowing' and describing the properties of food and their actions. There are diet cures suggested for cancer, for multiple sclerosis, even suggestions that diet may influence resistance to Aids. There are nutrition programmes to improve your skin, to stop your hair falling out or going grey, to reduce noise in the inner ear, to improve your memory. There are colleges, therapists and schools dedicated to teaching the science of nutrition or providing you with your Personal Health Programme, a programme, incidentally, which carries the mock warning This Programme May Seriously Improve Your Health.[5]

Nor has there ever been a time when understanding what you eat has been invested with such significance, becoming the activity on which your whole health and well-being, possibly even your life, depend. Doubtless in the same way that we now view the Victorian era as peculiarly obsessed with sex and hygiene (often together), future historians will not be able to overlook the absolute obsession which we, in a culture of plenty, have with what goes into our bellies and bodies. In the 1950s and 1960s, the discussion of sexuality had long changed from the Victorian emphasis on controlling or denying debasing sexual impulses. By then the concern was much more with understanding, releasing or satisfying these impulses, and with freeing ourselves from the shame which had previously cloaked them. Nevertheless, it would be no exaggeration to say that sexuality, whether it was to be repressed or released, has, over the last century, been taken to be the single most intriguing element of our physical beings. The great mystery and obsessive question was to understand the human sexual response. Our ability to cope or not with our sexual responses was likely to be the single most important element in our psychic well-being. And our inability to cope was likely to be the source of all guilt and anxiety.

How dramatically these values have changed! If, during the last century, the main concern about the body was sexuality and how our sexual impulses connected with our personalities, now all that has changed. Food, and its relation to health, has totally replaced sex as the major source of public anxiety about the body. Now the main thing to know about the body in Western society is what and how it eats and how that connects with health. Food and how it interacts with the complex chemical chains of the body is seen as the most important physical aspect of ourselves as human beings. Food, we are told, is responsible for just about everything; it will explain illness, health, personality, even social behaviour. Claims for the power of food extend far beyond individual good health. Food is the route to perfection in physical health, the solution to all forms of disability, social decay and disorder.

The solution to disability

The first step towards perfection which food can apparently decide is the end of old age. A longer life, we are told, can be achieved through a rigorous, almost scientific, attitude towards food. First, you must eat according to the principles of a healthy diet to avoid major diseases: 'you can easily learn enough about how to use nutritional knowledge to protect yourself to a large extent against the many dreaded degenerative diseases of our time.'[6] Then you must supplement your diet with the various minerals and substances whose reduction appears to be associated with the epiphenomena of growing old, such as greying of hair, wrinkling of skin, loss of memory and senility. Finally, you could opt for the more extreme food strategies, like those of Roy Walford, author of *Live to One Hundred*, who claims to have found procedures which 'definitively slow or decelerate the rate of ageing: caloric undernutrition and lowering the internal body temperature'.[7]

These strategies are not just the stuff of harmless fantasies in magazine articles. In the United States they are actually offered as 'anti-senility' or 'longevity' programmes, with colleges and courses devoted to the pursuit of the perfect diet. Dr Downes, for example, suggests that 'a well-planned nutritional programme that is specifically designed from the forties until the end of our life span, may not make us live for ever, but it will definitively slow down the ageing process and add years to our lives.' Dr Hoffer in similar vein offers an anti-senility diet. 'Everyone,' he says, 'owes it to himself and his family to live the kind of life that will minimize the possibility of becoming senile. The way to do this is to make sure that you get your nutrition under control at least by the time you are forty, if not before. If we all did this, within twenty years we could begin to close down our nursing homes and bring the problem of senility under control.'[8]

Lurking behind the fantasies of immortality is another message. There is a hidden agenda that improved diet will remove the *problem* of age. In other words an anti-senility programme is not just of benefit to the individual but to society at large since the need for caring for elderly dependants will apparently be removed. What characterizes this movement is a horror of old age, and of dependency and a general sense that these conditions are abhorrent and burdensome. At one level these attitudes are simply typical of the society in which they circulate. Western society in general views such attributes as burdensome. Yet something more complex is going on. In these new discourses about food, solutions are being offered at the level of the individual body and its health, rather than at the level of society. Instead of finding ways in which old age or dependency could become less of a 'problem', we are being told that we could eradicate the problem through transformations of individual health.

This implicit propaganda for the power of food to solve social problems is very much more explicit in other areas. If claims for a longer life span are characterized by a sort of egocentric Utopianism, claims about social behaviour are both grander and more worrying. Originating in studies which connected 'hyperactivity' in children with allergies to specific additives and lack of proper diet, much more drastic ideas have developed. These ideas have revived the old-fashioned idea of juvenile delinquency and linked it to a bad diet:

Ecological and sociological changes in this country since the end of World War II have not been positive for child-rearing. The pattern for young people includes declining educational performance and increasing rates of suicide, drug and alcohol abuse, chronic illness, delinquency and violent behaviour . . . Accompanying this has been the constant and substantial deterioration of the quality of the diet.[9]

These ideas connecting certain types of 'anti-social' behaviour with specific nutritional deficiencies have been pioneered in America. But such ideas are now widespread. In England, for example, the Biosocial Therapy Association argues that the brain is the first organ to be affected by malnutrition and since the brain controls impulses and behaviour we can look to diet as the explanation for forms of anti-social behaviour.[10] These studies even link particular kinds of mineral or chemical imbalances to particular kinds of anti-social behaviour, for example, 'lack of folic acid results in a lack of fear of social consequences'.[11] Although these studies have made useful links between allergies, poor nutrition and the problems experienced by some children, they nevertheless have alarming implications. Their stance is intensely normative, with no attempt to question the social and behavioural values which they wish all children to conform to. At no point is there any question about the inadequacies of the society or authorities against which certain behaviour is directed. The only problem with society itself, it appears, is the consumption of junk food.

A similarly sinister development is in 'pre-conceptual' care. Numerous books on pregnancy and childbirth stress the importance of an optimum pre-conceptual diet. The mother must be in perfect physical health to give her child the best chance of 'being healthy'. Indeed, there is an increasing implication that a woman should not become pregnant until she has made her body ready, getting rid of impurities and pursuing optimum nutrition in order to give her child the best chance of perfect health. 'The many degenerative diseases generally associated with later years in life do not happen overnight. They probably have their beginnings in early childhood, if not before birth.'[12] There is even a University of the Womb in California, where parents are told to pay attention to their diet as the cornerstone in building the edifice of the 'advanced' or 'gifted' child. The explicit theory behind this is that a child who is more forward will suffer from fewer frustrations than an ordinary child. The implicit message, however, is 'greedier'. It suggests again a society where an individual can have and achieve everything, where frustration cannot and need not be tolerated.

Latent in the idea of planning for pregnancy is an abhorrence of the 'abnormal' or disabled child. It is part of the general move in Western culture towards the perfect, the obliteration of everything which reminds us of problems, disease, dependency. The implications of writings on pregnancy are part and parcel of this general elevation of diet, and the linking of diet with perfectible health. There is a definite eugenicist strand, suggesting that only the perfect should be allowed to be born, which simply takes the concern with perfection to its logical conclusion. In all these writings there runs a theme of the possibility of perfectible health, and the role of nutrition in accompanying this. There is a push towards the abolition of disease, disorderly bodies, and perhaps even death, with food elevated as the solution of all these problems. Instead of any push to organize society to cope with differences, disability and dependency, there is a push to obliterate them and to establish health as the norm to which each individual has a duty to conform. The individual body has been elevated through this concern with food to being the place where social solutions can be found.

Nowhere can the distance between affluent parts of the world and the poor be more clearly marked than in this new significance given to food. In a peculiarly perverse movement, a divided world is united in its concern with food, yet the meanings for the individuals in these countries is quite different. In the Third World, as well as in the affluent countries, food is connected with death. Yet in our affluent countries, food has come to be associated with the abolition of death, and is surrounded with the symbolism of perfectibility. For the poor, food is the difference between survival and starvation. For the rich countries, food marks the difference between self-inflicted decay and perfect health. In the affluent West, food has now been attributed with all the meanings previously associated with sex; it represents a dangerous area where the individual can and should exercise control. If he or she doesn't then guilt and illness will probably follow. Yet it is only in the culture of extreme affluence that food could possibly be linked to individual choice and the freedom to determine the health of the individual body.

Food awareness

It is clear that in all these theories, nutrition has acquired overwhelming, perhaps even magical, significance. It is the clue to individual and social health. Yet the concept of nutrition now is very different from that imagined for us by science-fiction visions of eating in the late twentieth century. In the 1960s, films and novels contained fantasies of the future where food was always replaced by the nutrition tablet containing all that was necessary for the perfect diet. Food as such would have been definitively downgraded, leaving humans free to concern themselves with the far frontiers of space. Obviously such a development is scientifically possible and the infamous diet formulas are prepared on just such a basis. But nothing could be further from contemporary discussions of nutrition. Of course vitamin 'supplementation' is widespread, and profitable for those involved in it. There is also widespread research into isolating or developing certain nutritional elements which may be used in the treatment of individuals. But for the most part this work and research is aimed always at supplementing, never replacing food. *Food* not only remains crucial but has in fact increased its centrality and significance.

Indeed, far from 'the science of nutrition' spelling the end to the satisfactions to be derived from food, consciousness about a healthy diet involves the opposite. Eating food has become a heightened experience and the preparation of food and the ritual of meals have become *more* important rather than less. 'Heightened food awareness' is not as might be suspected a joke but a serious recommendation from some highly respected exponents of holistic living. Patrick Pietroni, for instance, recommends a 'conscious-eating exercise' where you sit down in front of your plate, make yourself comfortable, shut your eyes, allow your breathing to become relaxed and rhythmical and then 'encounter' your food.

. . . pick up a piece of fruit with your fingers, become aware of the textures and edges – pause for a few moments. Then bring the fruit to just below your nose and take in any smells. Try and see if you can pick out different smells from different parts of the fruit – pause for a moment and become aware of any changes in your breathing. Now bring the fruit to your lips and tongue and explore the fruit again . . . etc. The aim of the exercise is to relax and to become conscious of why and how we are eating.[13]

This idea had filtered down into the women's magazines as a good way of reducing weight – the more conscious you are of each piece of food, the less you will want to eat.

This attention to how we eat and the rituals governing eating is evidenced through the various strands of writing on healthy diet. Some of the attention is deeply faddist. *Fit for Life* and *Food Combining for Health* both recommend that when and how you eat is more important than what you eat. They argue that only certain types of food should be combined, otherwise the body exhausts too much energy trying to digest inappropriate combinations of food. The basis for this argument is that it is not natural to combine foods; animals don't so humans shouldn't. The increasingly fashionable macrobiotic diet is similarly definite that its recommendations are not just about the food but about adopting a whole cuisine and life style.

The correct preparation of foods is so important that everyone should learn how to cook the macrobiotic way either by attending classes or under the guidance of an experienced macrobiotic cook . . . View everything and everyone you meet with gratitude, particularly offering thanks before and after each meal. Please chew your food well, at least fifty times per mouthful.[14]

If these recommendations seem peculiar they are only the extreme end of the concern with attitude towards food and life style which dominates the literature on healthy living. Heightened consciousness about food is not just about what the food is but about the rituals around preparation and eating of food. Heightened consciousness is about being fully aware of the significance of food.

This emphasis on the importance of life style, preparation, and consciousness of food point to the immense symbolic significance of healthy eating. Clearly there is more being swallowed than simply a balanced combination of vitamins and minerals. Those who believe so passionately in 'healthy eating' clearly also believe that they are ingesting attributes which require conscious attention, and a whole series of governing rituals. After all, the basic elements of what is supposed to constitute a healthy diet have changed little over the course of this century. But 'healthy eating' has, over the last decade, become a weightier pursuit requiring serious attention to nutrition and heightened food awareness. The question which arises confronted with all the significance attached to eating healthily is what exactly are the meanings associated with health foods? What do we believe we are eating when, in the late twentieth century, we change our diet as the first, and most important step to new health?

The meanings of health foods

It is, of course, the case that all food in every culture where starvation is not the central problem has symbolic significance. Indeed food is very often associated with religious rituals and observances, as in the 'tradition' of eating fish on Fridays in European culture. What food means to the consumer is almost as significant as what it is. In fact it is difficult to separate the two. And this is undoubtedly the case with health foods. The fact that taste is culturally shaped and socially controlled is well known, not just to anthropologists, but even to advertisers who recognize that consumers more often than not make choices between brands based not on taste but on image or the meanings of a particular brand. 'A basic finding in product research,' writes Julia Lannon,

> is that the ability to discriminate between tastes (although not textures) is very blunt indeed. This is demonstrated through either blind taste tests of different foods or, more interestingly, tests of the same food in different guises. For example, a sample of 100 housewives showed a significant preference for a piece of meat labelled English lamb compared to a piece of meat labelled New Zealand lamb when, in fact, both pieces were cut from the same New Zealand joint. Changing the packaging can change the taste.[15]

Numerous factors are important in food, other than the satisfaction of hunger or the provision of exact nutritional requirements. In fact it has been shown how stressing the nutritional and beneficial values of certain foods is to no avail if the food contravenes other symbolic or cultural expectations. This was the fate of 'textured soya protein' when it was originally marketed towards poor families as a substitute for meat. In spite of its cheapness and great claims for healthiness it was considered unacceptable. Yet packaged as a health food, deriving from ancient oriental cuisine, tofu (made from the same basic ingredients) is extremely popular. The choice of a food, and the satisfaction it brings, is determined often by the symbolic level, that is, by what each piece of food (or its combination) means to the eater. 'Health' food is certainly no exception to the idea that food satisfies more than bodily need. Many individuals might claim that they have chosen consciously to pursue a healthy diet because it has been scientifically proven to be at the basis of good health. Yet the pursuit of health through diet is as deeply implicated in food symbolism as any complicated system of religious observances and taboos on certain foods.

Perhaps the most striking aspect of 'health foods' is that they carry the implication of group allegiance, which is very strong both to those inside and outside the group. To eat healthily is by definition to be different from the dominant food culture. Nowadays, group allegiance is rarely expressed by food preference except for the allegiance to certain foods within ethnic, or religious, groups. Other social differences tend to be expressed through other aspects of lifestyle like the type of drink or the use of a particular drug. Yet 'good nutrition' in the health movement carries connotations of an overall approach to life which is supposed to be counter to the values by which the 'majority' live, the values, that is, of consumerism and 'junk' foods. What is implicit in this hostility to the 'dominant' pattern of eating in our society is a criticism of mass society, a criticism of the passive consumers of industrialized society, where a 'healthy' attitude towards food becomes a way of supposedly reasserting individuality.

Until very recently certain groups regarded 'health food' as undesirable precisely because it suggested an alternative (and therefore odd) life style. The connotations carried for example by brown bread actually deterred certain groups from buying it in spite of a widespread acceptance that it was healthier or 'virtuous'.

. . . white bread is 'normal'; it is something you depend on and are used to as part of the daily routine. It is simply 'there' to be used; it does not interfere as brown bread is perceived to do. Extreme projections of 'women who use only brown bread' seen through the eyes of users of white bread were most revealing. 'Health food addicts', 'cranky', 'faddy', 'obsessed with their bowels', 'odd in some ways' were the terms that women used, illustrating the psychological distance from 'normal' women with 'ordinary' families and values. It appeared that the cultural history of brown bread as *virtuous* was contributing to the social distancing of it from the habits of ordinary women.[16]

Nowadays these values appear to have suffered a direct inversion. The healthy eaters are no longer the hippie fringe or faddists but those who have taken responsibility for their health.

Actually, consciousness about healthy eating can in no way be properly described as alternative these days. The expansion of health food shops and vegetarian restaurants, the growth of wholefood manufacturers (like Plamil and Realeat) and the success of a number of vegetarian magazines (such as the *Vegetarian*, *Green Cuisine* and *Lean Living*) all signal the widespread acceptance of these ideas. Moreover, instead of dismissal of health foods as faddist, there is a prevailing social guilt about not being sufficiently attentive to healthy eating. All these factors indicate that consciousness about the principles of the health movement has spread deeply into society even if the average British family doesn't follow the rules. Even so, the conscious pursuit of health through diet signals to those involved that they belong to an 'enlightened' and 'progressive' group, and is enormously important in people's motivation to 'eat healthily'. 'Conscious eating' signals a distance from, perhaps even a rebellion against, the passive acceptance of mass society embodied in the much reviled 'junk' food.

A sense of social position, perhaps even a morality, seems to be at stake in the commitment to healthy eating. And it is easy to see a division of the world into the virtuous and the naughty in the oppositions which are set up between 'healthy' food and 'junk' food. In this infantile splitting of the world, most foods associated with pure satisfaction of taste (that is most of the sugary or sweet foods) fall on to the side of the wicked. Frequently writers or commentators conjure up a vision of 'the masses', that is, people who only eat 'junk' and 'rubbish'. 'My own experience', writes an apparently health-conscious Paul Levy in the *Observer*, 'shows that there cannot be very many children in Britain who are not getting enough of what my children call "naughty food". ' Although those in the health movement apparently want to change the nation's diet, the notion of their difference from other groups is crucial. Notions of 'healthy' eating may dominate most contemporary discourses on food, but nevertheless the satisfactions involved in 'healthy eating' feed on these very clear meanings of opposition, difference and by implication superiority. What is at stake is a hostility to and rejection of a vision of mass society. Yet the only thing that is criticized is the way the *body* is treated and its resultant disorders. There has been virtually no criticism of social divisions in society and certainly no sustained critique of how food production and marketing is organized.

The raw and the cooked

The division of food into bad and good, virtuous and naughty is crucial in the hierarchies and significant oppositions which surround ideas about healthy eating. The principles of this hierarchy and opposition are relatively consistent and concise. Indeed, beneath the mountains of literature on the subject, lies a quite simple, widely agreed idea of what constitutes a basic healthy diet.

> One, the foods eaten should be whole foods and not fractions of foods, which are the products of refining. Two, foods should be as fresh as possible; they should be allowed as little time for deterioration, which is often the result of oxidation. This means 'the food should be as close to a living state as possible' because cooking increases the carcinogenic properties of foods. Three, the food should be non-toxic – that is, it should not contain synthetic flavours, colours, preservatives or other additives that cosmetically enhance the food. And four, the diet should be variable, because people have adapted to a wide range of foods that offer a broad selection of nutrients.[17]

The 'bad' foods are animal fats, sugar, refined grains and processed food. The 'good' foods are rich in fibre, are always 'whole' – like whole wheat and whole meal – or they are seeds, grains or pulses. Raw food like fruit or vegetables is particularly virtuous, or where cooked then only minimally. Quite often animal protein of any kind is bad. But there are numerous 'demi-vegies' where the call for food to be as 'close as possible to the living state' is curiously reversed. There is instead a hierarchy of meats with the 'white' meats of chicken and fish more acceptable than red and bloody meats.

There is, of course, plenty of evidence that over-cooking destroys essential nutrients in food, and that forms of industrial processing do remove nutrients which are now recognized as healthy, such as the processing of white flour. Nevertheless the magical qualities attributed to healthy eating seem to confirm that the foods' virtues are as much symbolic as they are 'evidential'. Food scientists, for example, argue both that natural foods can be poisonous and that there are more dangers in the natural decomposition of foods. They add that the limitations imposed by relying on the fresh possibly outweigh the dangers from industrialized processes. Absolute reliance on the raw or fresh, they claim, can lead to situations of scarcity, or unvarying diet, since diet would become dependent on seasonal availability. Of course, in an affluent society like our own, there are always supplies of fresh fruit and vegetables from around the world. But then the food scientists point out that transporting by jumbo jet would seem to qualify as an industrialized rather than a 'natural' process. There is also the cruel irony, revealed by one research project, that those showing the lowest pesticide residues were 'those living on a "junk food diet", excluding vegetables, fruit and cereals.' The wholesome diet of fresh vegetables and unprocessed cereals of the past must be called into question by modern farming methods.[18]

When it comes to processing, food scientists are equally convinced that there are major advantages to be set against the high level of risk perceived by those opposed to all forms of processing. There is, for example, the suggestion that 'there are factory techniques in which . . . losses [of vitamins] are reduced so that total losses are less than those incurred when raw products are cooked at home.'[19] Frozen peas, the food scientists tell us, lose fewer vitamins when cooked for the very brief periods required than do fresh peas which require longer cooking. The food scientists also argue that the advantages from preservation, like canning or freezing, which delays or halts microbiotic decay very much outweigh the risks of illness from these processes. There is obviously good reason to be suspicious of some of the positions offered by the food scientists given their close relation to the food industry. Nevertheless, their objections have to be looked at seriously. Clearly both groups, those hostile to mass-produced food and those profiting by it, have a different perception of the risks to health. And this perception of risks relates both to different values about health and the body and to the symbolism attaching to the different foods.

The major health concern of the food industry is hygiene, but this is no longer true for the new healthy eaters. Far more important now is the avoidance of the many dreaded 'degenerative diseases of our time'.[20] 'Healthy eaters' insist that the cause of these diseases is industrially and mass-produced food. Indeed in the symbolic language attaching to health foods there is an ungovernable hostility to processed food, and to any industrialized techniques applied to food. 'The foods for which man is adapted are not refined, artificially preserved, or concentrated, as are so many of those consumed nowadays by civilized human beings. Therefore a return to health demands food as naturally occurring as possible.'[21] Everywhere there are references to the damaging effects of processing. The hostility to industrialized food production is not just hostility to the use of additives and preservatives, but also hostility to the processes of refinement and preserving themselves which are seen as generally depleting the food to a point of virtual worthlessness.

Running through ideas about healthy eating is the desire to minimize the intervention of processing between the food from the field and the meal. Cooking, once regarded as the highest human art, is in these accounts a rather problematic activity, even being viewed at moments as a sort of mini-industrial process. Writing about the virtues of raw foods, for instance, Charles Gerras in *Feasting on Raw Foods* describes them as 'unfired foods' and then goes on to define raw as anything not heated beyond 60 degrees, on the grounds that this is the temperature of water from the average domestic hot water tap. It is a strange distinction since heated tap water certainly seems to be a highly industrialized commodity, but his distinction rests on the lack of compositional changes to food before reaching that heat. Cooking, we are told, using human skills and human utensils, is far more likely to transform the 'nature' of the food.

It is symptomatic that there has been no criticism of the relations of domesticity along with this criticism of cooking. In fact, there is a paradoxical emphasis on the importance of domestic production, often to the point where nothing is considered nutritionally valuable unless directly prepared in the home. Home Milling Enterprises, drawing on prevailing health food beliefs about the rapid 'degeneration' of stored flour, argue that 'only fresh milling guarantees you all the goodness of grain.'[22] And those who advocate sprouting beans at home do so because the food can be eaten so freshly. It is as if the home itself had become a miniature world, in which the individual may forage and prepare without the intervention of the modern world. This hostility to anything industrial and praise of the home is symptomatic of the way all social criticism in the alternative health movement is focused on generalized social forces called 'technological society', 'industrial society' or 'mass society'. All the problems of society are seen as resulting from the unrestrained development of the machine and the lack of individuality, embodied in 'mass production' of food. There is a complete disregard for more specific social divisions, and the problems they create, divisions like the sexual division of labour in the home. For the home, and the division of labour within the home, is one of the baselines on which women's socially inferior status is built. Yet the preference for home preparation is sublimely oblivious to the fact that it implies more work in the kitchen, which will doubtless be carried out by women.

Hostility to cooked food while simultaneously valuing the skills of domestic production is not quite as contradictory as it might first appear. What is important in the rejection of the values of industrialized production is not hostility to domestic work but rather the development of a significant opposition between the raw and the cooked. Raw food, that which has not been cooked or processed, has assumed a hitherto unparalleled significance.

> With this greater awareness [of healthy eating] has come a heightened interest in new ways of preparing food rich in nutrients and truly natural flavours. One of the simplest and best cuisines of all has gone largely unnoticed and its core is literally

and figuratively in our own garden – the fresh tasting, wonderfully nourishing, palate-tingling world of raw foods.[23]

The raw and the processed are seen as the opposition between the natural (good) and the technological (bad). It is a reversal of precisely the thinking which saw refined (and therefore distant from nature) as good because it expressed those fundamentally human skills of cooking and processing.

Thus we have a situation where *preparation* is all-important. Cooking, however, in the form of heating and transforming the original structure of the food is seen as much more problematic, possibly even dangerous, a position embodied in Leslie Kenton's warning that 'cooking may damage your health'. It is as if anything which comes from the industrialized world might taint and 'destroy' the qualities of food. This hostility to cooking as a sort of small-scale industrial activity derives from an opposition between raw and cooked food. This opposition between the raw and the cooked is hardly an opposition new to human society, though the meanings attached to the two and the balance between them shifts in different societies and at different moments of history. The opposition is one which the anthropologist Claude Lévi-Strauss has shown to be fundamental in all the world's cuisines. He argues that although eating for survival is a 'natural' activity, that is, shared with the animals, cooking is a fundamentally human activity and is therefore an expression of culture. Animals forage, eating what they find as they find it and need it. Humans preserve, store and prepare, and invest the eating of food with social significance. Thus he sees the preparation of food as lying at a fundamental point of intersection for humans, the intersection between nature and culture. He sees the transformation of nature through cooking as an expression of humanity's social and cultural identity, in short an expression of our difference from nature.

However, the difference between nature and culture is not absolute or fixed for humanity. It is constantly to be negotiated and differs between different societies.

As a species we are animal, more or less like other animal species; we have parallel bodily functions and similar bodily requirements for survival. At the same time, however, we are not animal but human. We have language, intelligence, and culture blended in a way that is unique to this planet. We are creatures of 'nature' and 'culture' simultaneously. Moreover, knowledge of this universal feature of human beings is itself universal and forms part of the 'cultural awareness' of all societies. Yet it is also a source of latent tension in human affairs which, Lévi-Strauss suggests, perennially demands resolution.[24]

What Lévi-Strauss suggests is that the way in which food is prepared and cooked expresses how that difference between nature and culture is interpreted by any particular society or group within that society.

Nothing could be more vividly illuminating when dealing with current ideas about healthy eating. Here the balance has tipped in favour of the raw, in favour of food which has been exposed as little as possible to any human intervention. The cultural, or what is distinctly human, is regarded as dangerous, possibly even 'polluting' in exactly the same way that certain foods are regarded as polluting in certain religions, for example, pork for Jews and meat for Sikhs. Only minimal intervention between nature and human consumption is encouraged. The aim is to allow the natural components of food to feed the human body with their essential energies unimpeded by cultural taint. 'The radiance and energy of the sun is captured within [the] cells [of whole, fresh food], bringing to you an energy and liveliness that is not available through any other nutritional pathway. Food which has been processed or packaged has been adulterated.'[25] Latent in these ideas is a view of the *plant* as encapsulating the life forces of nature. 'Seeds', for example, 'are a storehouse of energy, vitamins and minerals for the baby plant.'[26] The closer food can come to the life force of the growing plant, the greater its value as food.

One can hardly miss the development of a whole cuisine based on raw 'baby' plants, such as maize, courgettes, and aubergines. New York restaurants heap bowls with salads of 'baby' plants. Visually delightful they may be, but they are barely edible by those unmoved by the moral quest for vigorous and life-giving forces in their food. What is more, certain salad foods like tomatoes have the highest pesticide levels of any foods. Herbs, too, have acquired properties far beyond those of flavouring; they are 'life-giving' plants *par excellence*, linked as they are with traditional healing methods. 'Herbs are beneficial to the human race simply because they were specifically created to alleviate human complaints. Almost all of them have restorative properties, rather than destructive ones. Creation meant them to be so, and when they are expertly combined together they can be of great advantage to us and without any side effects.'[27]

This favouring of 'nature' over 'culture' and the distrust of human activities is the embodiment of the views of nature discussed earlier in this book. 'Nature' is defined as that which is life-giving. Nature is not about death or decay. It is about birth, renewal, and vigorous growth – all the properties supposedly contained in the growing plant or better still the 'baby' plant. Nature is not about monstrosity, savagery, or the wicked tricks of poisoning and accidents. This is abundantly clear in the different assessment of 'risks' from food. For the food scientists nature is still 'risky' and has to be rendered hygienic by technology even if this means bombarding animals and plants with outrageously high doses of antibiotics and chemicals. For 'healthy eaters', nature carries no such risk; the risks from culture are far greater. For one group danger is located in nature, in the other it is located in culture. And it is clear that, with the widespread acceptance of the current principles of healthy eating, views of nature as beneficient and culture as dangerous are now in the ascendancy.

Avoidance of meat and the energetic properties of natural food

Nothing makes clearer this reconceptualization of nature than new attitudes towards meat eating. Avoidance of animal flesh is the other side to praising plants. This is partly because animals are seen as similarly subject to 'intervention', 'processing' and 'industrialization'. Animals are kept in 'factory' farms, herded together and able to survive without disease in these conditions because of continual doses of pretherapeutic antibiotics. Thus animal flesh has been subject to excessively dangerous human intervention. But there is more at stake in the contemporary avoidance of meat. It is also a reworking of a theme as old as humanity itself since all societies invest meat eating with symbolic significance, although the specific meanings attached to different meats vary from culture to culture.

Anthropological studies have suggested that red meats tend to be associated in various societies and in various ways with sexuality, carnality, strength and death. For instance 'it is still the practice in some parts of southern Spain for a woman to go to the butcher following a bull-fight to buy a steak from the bravest bull for her husband's supper, thus ensuring his continued strength and manliness'.[28] In Britain, even if we do not go to those extremes, the bloodiness of meat is taken as some sort of expression of power which puts red meat at the top of a hierarchy of foods. In 'traditional' British attitudes this hierarchy meant that red meat was considered the most valuable food.

> The basis of this hierarchy . . . is both status and some sort of power. At the top, highest in status there stand the 'red' meats – steak, roast beef; lower down are the white or bloodless meats – chicken, fish; and below them, animal products such as eggs. The high status items figure as the centrepiece of meals, though cheese and eggs are the centrepiece of lighter meals, snacks or supper. On the next level down the hierarchy come the vegetables – regarded in our family system as the adjuncts, insufficient to form a meal alone without some sort of flesh or animal product as the focus.[29]

Although subconsciously meat is invested with this power, most British people do not enjoy seeing the blood in their meat, and cook joints of lamb and beef until the blood ceases to be visible liquid. Most people are also repelled by the idea of eating carnivorous animals such as cats, dogs, crows, though there are some societies which do. It is as if red meat carries the connotation of strength, carnality and death, and the idea of eating carnivores is felt to be eating 'too strong' meat. Contemporary writing on healthy eating actually shares the values of this hierarchy, even if they are inverted. Instead of making red meat the most valuable, it is the least. Nevertheless, red meat is still attributed with the greatest power albeit negative and destructive power.

This is well illustrated by the widespread demi-vegetarian tendency. Quite unlike ethical vegetarianism, this pre-vegetarian stratum does eat meat but mainly 'white' meats like fish and chicken. The crucial factor here is that of blood. Certain meats are seen as too bloody, too overtly reminiscent of the power which red meat is thought to have. There is more at stake here than an assertion that excessive consumption of meat and animal fats is not only unhealthy but also ecologically unsound. The writing is also riddled with a sense of disgust and repulsion at the idea of eating animal flesh, 'most of our illnesses can be . . . greatly relieved by the abstention from consuming the toxic ingredients of cooked flesh foods all our lives.'[30] In this view of 'natural' eating, it is thought that humanity must be in harmony with nature. Bloody meat is too openly a reminder of disharmony, of violent death. Meat expresses both cultural intervention and death and disharmony. All these elements are in open conflict with the life-enhancing and vigorous meanings of seeds and vegetables.

In the opposition between bad and virtuous foods there is another category. There are also magical foods, foods which are particularly well endowed with all the positive attributes of nature I have described. These foods are more than just virtuous like soya protein, tofu, seaweed, bean sprouts and lentils. Magical foods have magical attributes; they capture the vital energies of nature. Health stores abound in these special foods and substances like ginseng and Amazonian gurunga. Magic foods are always 'naturally occurring' and unprocessed. Royal jelly for instance 'is a unique and vital substance produced by the worker bee only until the 10th day of its life and fed to the queen bee who quickly attains perfect physical development, with a life span of five years. Meanwhile the worker bees existing on normal nutrient grow to half the size with a life span of forty days only . . . This seemingly miraculous product of Nature, is not processed in any way . . .' and contains 'a proportion in it which defies scientific definition'. Taken daily it can 'help one attain better health, vitality, youthful energy and radiance' and taken over a period of three months this miracle food can bring 'incredible improvement in general health, and well-being, revitalizing complexion and hair'.[31]

Often such magical foods have an ancestry; they were known about by 'primitive' groups, a secret held for millennia, like, for example, tea-tree oil, advertised as having been used by the Australian Aborigines. Nothing seems to lend greater credence to a food or tonic than if it has been used at some point by 'primitives', 'monks' or 'holy men'. Substance preparation is greatly enhanced if presided over by some venerable or hermit-like being in touch with the natural mysteries. Pelgor Herbs, for example, 'are hand picked when they are at their prime by the old age pensioners . . . They are then sun-dried on a terrace rather than oven-dried. Franco, being an artist, then retires from the world for a few weeks while he is combining them together. (Sometimes he emerges with a long beard.)'[32] These ancient sages and primitive groups are represented as understanding the 'essential' qualities of nature. These people, we are led to believe, have hit on plants which embody all the beneficial attributes of nature, plants which mysteriously embody the raw, unprocessed, energetic qualities which a truly healthy diet should deliver.

The other end of nutrition

It is perhaps inevitable that such an obsessive preoccupation with what goes into the body, and how specific nutrients affect different organs, will be accompanied by a simultaneous preoccupation with what comes out of the body. No longer just a question of making sure that what goes into the body is invested with all the life-giving, energy-enhancing properties of nature, it is also necessary now to purge our bodies of the traces of industrialized corruptions. Audrey Eyton's F-Plan Diet was in fact the first indication that shit had become a major public preoccupation as opposed to a quirky fascination of a fringe group, or the private obsession of the multitude. But fibre at that point was the perfect solution to dieting without giving anything up, as revealed in the All-Bran advertisement 'Eat Yourself Fit'. Fibre is the food which can be eaten in bulk to satisfy hunger and which is largely passed out of the body.

But fibre and shit have now taken on an altogether grander significance. It is no longer a question of constipation versus the now polite sounding 'regularity'. Instead cleansing, flushing out and detoxification are the terms which dominate the 'other end' of nutrition. Constipation has become the worst of afflictions, allowing the build up of horrifying substances, putrefying food, indigestible remains and dangerous poisons. In this context excreting has become a major purification, a ritual expunging of the harmful side products of the food we eat. 'Most of the meat we eat

is injected, the fish is polluted, and fruit and vegetables are sprayed
. . . accumulation of toxins is responsible for most of the illnesses
from which we suffer. People believe that if they go regularly every
morning, that is perfectly proper and sufficient. Far from it –
proper elimination has to be selective and right down to fluid.'[33]
Indeed the modest request for 'once a day' has been replaced by a
much looser requirement of 'three times a day after meals'.[34]

In 1986, *Green Farm* magazine named the colon 'the organ of the
year'[35] on the grounds that 'practically everyone who calls or writes
is concerned about how theirs is functioning. This is hardly
surprising; if your colon isn't happy the rest of you won't be either,
and recently both research into and consciousness of this organ
have increased considerably.' If the colon has been heretofore 'this
neglected organ', the times have certainly changed in its favour
now. 'Colonics' or 'colon cleansing' are now widely offered as
necessary 'therapies' to achieve health. The programme offered is
usually 'an intensive routine designed to remove old sticky
putrefying material from the large intestine or colon'. This
lyricism about the build up of poisons and toxins in the colon is
common. The problem they tell us is both the production of non-
digestible residues which should be excreted, and the problem of
the inefficiency of the 'organs of elimination' particularly in the
light of the assault on them by 'toxins' in food and pollution in the
atmosphere.

It is, in fact, by no means the case that only the colon has been
singled out for these attentions, although it does seem to have a
special place in our hearts and minds. All the organs involved in
'elimination' – the lungs, the colon, the liver, kidneys and pancreas
– have become particularly significant in the quest for the
purification of the body. Many of the 'cures' offered for diseases
with which conventional medicine fails, are based on the cleansing
of the body, either by fasting or by radical diets based on fruit
juices. This is the basis of the apparently successful Gerson
therapy. Naturopathy also regularly suggests fasting as providing
'a digestive or physiological rest, during which the body is able to
devote all its energies to eliminating accumulations of waste matter
from the system'.[36]

This interest in excretion is linked closely with the overall effect
of our new preoccupation with health food. As with the interest in

vitamins and minerals and their relation to particular organs, interest in the organs of elimination is linked with the creation of a whole new inner geography of the body. Instead of the previous simple notion of food in our bellies, we now have a whole complex and detailed vision of the food broken down by various organs into chemicals and enzymes. Potentially, we could know every action of every acid, enzyme and chemical on every organ, and their interrelation. This knowledge has, if nothing else, opened up a whole inner geography of the body, a much larger inner space than previously. The body can be known minutely in its interior space in all the complexity of its workings.

This notion of an inner geography has opened up a highly individualized notion of the body. There is now even a notion of 'biochemical individuality'. In other words, the inner space of contemporary theories of nutrition is after all, a highly personal space. 'In the fields of diet and health no two people are exactly alike. The variable in the human metabolism appears to spread over a wide spectrum, so wide that what is nourishing for one person may be deleterious to another.'[37] And it is this notion of individuality which can save the alternative health movement from suggestions that the obsession with nutrition is too impersonal and scientific. Instead we are told that our biochemical individuality derives from heredity, environment, diet, life style and so on. Now institutes and therapists offer detailed individual analysis, through which they can correct imbalances, and make recommendations for the perfect diet tailored to your individual needs. These approaches can 'pinpoint an individual's exact nutritional needs and recommend the diet, food supplements and life style most suited to their metabolic type, thus eliminating the toxic substances that may have accumulated, restoring nutritional balance and paving the way to total health.'[38]

Conclusions

In this scenario, the interior of the body – its chemical interactions, its nutritional needs and the operations of ingestion, digestion and expulsion – can be known in highly individual ways. A new conception of the body and the person has opened up, an interior world of highly charged biochemical interactions. And each interaction is seen as crucial. It isn't just a matter of adequate health, it is a matter of life and death. Every mouthful you eat, every physical activity which you set in process has become crucial in the fight against the terrifying degenerative diseases of the Western world. It is curiously ironic in a moment of extreme affluence (but not equality) in Western nations, that food has become so immensely powerful, such a signifier of risk. Almost more than any other perceived risk, food has been foregrounded as bringing terrifying consequences if neglected.

And if the effect of food on the body is now perceived to be so crucial in the struggle between life and death, it is also the place where notions of individuality and individual responsibility have been enshrined again. Not only do we have to get to know our exact biochemical individuality but we have to know this in order to take personal responsibility for health. For in an affluent society food is all about choice. We eat according to our preferences and our tastes, however these might be conditioned by social meanings. And unlike many of the other factors which might make us ill, we do appear to have a large degree of choice over what we eat. Thus, eating health foods has become an activity where individuals feel they are making choices in *favour* of the virtues of nature, and *against* consumerism and mass society. It is here that attitudes towards food enter firmly into the realm of morality. According to this way of thinking, what we eat is about making choices, choices between illness and health, the perfect body as opposed to the obese, unhealthy or diseased body.

Food has become the all-important factor in the health of the body. It has acquired the most extreme powers in reversing ill health and winning good health. 'First class nutrition stands out [among factors determining our health] as the most important factor because it can minimize and keep in check the manifestations of hereditary weakness . . . can protect us against the harmful elements in our environment and the ravages of mental stress.'[39] Most importantly, food has become the channel *par excellence* where the individual can exercise personal responsibility. In the words of an American nutritionist working to improve the diet of schoolchildren: 'learning what to eat and why is an essential part of a child's education. You need your child's active co-operation, and s/he needs to understand something besides "it's good for you" so that s/he can take responsibility for his/her health improvement.'[40]

Yet this belief in the ability to *choose* individual health through diet is an illusion. The reason why increased awareness about food processing and food poisoning has caused such public panic is precisely because it undermines the introspective individualism of the food-to-health route. In a society where food production is highly industrialized, and where maximizing profits is the main consideration, even raw food has been submitted to processes way outside the consumers' control. In such a situation, the dream of transforming individual health, and therefore society, by eating 'a natural diet' is virtually meaningless. Any real attempt to improve food quality and health would also require a collective and political response to questions of how our environment, and therefore food production, are managed.

Notes

1 Manifesto of the British Naturopathic and Osteopathic Association 1987–8.
2 Quoted in the *Vegetarian*, July/August 1986.
3 Elyse Birkinshaw, *Turn Off Your Age*.
4 'Super Supplements', pamphlet no. 90 issued by Felmore Ltd.
5 Brochure issued by the Institute of Optimum Nutrition.
6 'Vitamins in Perspective', Felmore Ltd, pamphlet no. 14
7 'Longer Lifespan', Felmore Ltd, pamphlet no. 84.
8 'Keeping the Mind Young', Felmore Ltd, pamphlet no. 44.
9 'Nutrition and Your Kids', Felmore Ltd, pamphlet no. 126.
10 Lecture by Gail Bradley of the Bio-Social Therapy Association, given at the Exhibition of Alternative Health, 1987.
11 ibid.
12 Emory W. Thurston, *The Parent's Guide to Better Nutrition for Tots to Teenagers*.
13 Pietroni, op. cit.
14 Information leaflet on Macrobiotic Cookery.
15 J. Lannon, 'How People Choose Food' in Ritson et al. (eds), *The Food Consumer*, op. cit.
16 ibid.
17 'Keeping the Mind Young', op. cit.

18 'Chemicals in Farming', the *Vegetarian* magazine, July 1986.

19 R. Bralsford, 'Food Processing' in Ritson et al. (eds), *The Food Consumer*, op. cit.

20 Moule, op. cit.

21 ibid.

22 Advertisement for Home Milling Enterprises.

23 Charles Gerras (ed.), *Feasting on Raw Foods*.

24 Murcott, op. cit.

25 'Nutrition and Your Kids', op. cit.

26 Charles Gerras, op. cit.

27 'The Magic Story of Pelgor Herbs', promotional brochure.

28 Murcott, op. cit.

29 ibid.

30 Livingstone, op. cit.

31 Advertisement for Royal Jelly.

32 'The Magic Story of Pelgor Herbs', op. cit.

33 ibid.

34 Lecture by Dr Milo Siewert at the Exhibition of Alternative Medicine, 1987.

35 *Green Farm* magazine, 1986.

36 Manifesto of the British Naturopathic and Osteopathic Association, op. cit.

37 Tom and Carole Valentine, *Medicine's Missing Link: Metabolic Typing and Your Personal Food Plan*.

38 ibid.

39 'Vitamins in Perspective', op. cit.

40 'Nutrition and Your Kids', op. cit.

6 Women and Nature

Women occupy a special place in the contemporary obsession with natural life styles. Not only do women predominate in the natural health movement, but people connected with this movement believe that women have a privileged relation to nature. In particular women have become a significant linchpin in the new ideologies of the body's instinctive knowledge of natural health. While it is clearly not the case that all practitioners of alternative therapies have views on women and nature, nevertheless there is a significant tendency to see women as having a closer relation to nature and a finer understanding of natural laws. Some people even view the history of women as symptomatic of the whole lamentable history of conventional attitudes towards the body. Because the development of modern science and technology has coincided with a period of male dominance, then women can be seen as less tainted with industrial values and therefore more in touch with nature.

Now there is even a strand of feminism which sees the history of women, and women's bodies, as synonymous with the history of alternative medicine. Indeed, we are told in Charlene Spretnak's *The Politics of Women's Spirituality* that an understanding of 'the victimization' of women's bodies 'by allopathic medicine' will be the first step to discovering a whole series of new 'feminine' knowledges, knowledges that will connect us with all sorts of radical, feminist politics,

> new healings, the introduction of feminist uses of the martial arts
> . . . learnings about the laying on of hands, about loving,

healing, new seeings about health, nutrition, natural cures, connections between physical health and psychological realities, questions about reproduction, midwifery, parthenogenesis, self-nurturing and mothering; the Earth herself and the healing of her ten-thousand-year rape – the tending to the ground, farming, food production, relationship to animals, to plants and artefacts . . . a new assessment of the significance and destiny of a species which has ravaged its own home.[1]

While many of the adherents to alternative medicine would be somewhat put out by this conflation of their 'arts' with a ragbag of radical feminist aspirations, there are nevertheless significant points of overlap in the various movements. Indeed, this linking of ideas from feminism and the alternative health movement has tended to supply some exponents of each movement with a theory, a history and a politics. By a sleight of hand, the possibility of people ever achieving natural health has come to be associated with whether or not 'feminine' values can succeed over 'masculine' ones. Women will be able to supply a lost knowledge about the body and natural laws, about health, about nutrition, about how people should relate to each other. Although this new linking of women with nature appears to elevate women into a position of power, we will see in the ensuing chapter that the way that this has happened is highly dubious. Indeed in many ways these new ideas are symptomatic of the general tendencies which I have been discussing in this book. For instead of the convergence of feminism and alternative health movements producing a sharper politics in each, a whole new, profoundly problematic mythology of women has arisen.

Women and natural health

It is clear that women themselves have been drawn to the alternative health movement in greater numbers than men, even though this is by no means a sex-specific movement. Obviously the sex ratio varies from practice to practice but there are certain 'therapies' where women greatly predominate. Women, it seems, are drawn to those areas like aromatherapy and reflexology, the arts with close connections to beauty and massage treatment, or to the more 'mystical' pursuits like faith healing and psychic diagnosis. Men, on the other hand, tend to predominate in the more 'scientific' practices like homoeopathy. I was told by the director of one natural health clinic, in which aromatherapy and reflexology were central, that the majority of their students were women. She went on to specify that many of the women coming to her had similar backgrounds. They were in their late thirties or forties with children who had grown up and left home. Or they were recently divorced. Frequently the fees for the course were supplied either by the husband or from money which had come to the woman in the divorce settlement. For almost all, the course offered the chance of a new start, pursuing something that really interested them which might lead to a career. All seemed to see the course as 'doing something for myself' (perhaps for the first time), something which represented their 'true' interests which had been denied previous expression.

It should come as no surprise to find women strongly represented in a movement where health and the body are the principal concerns. After all, one of the most visible aspects of sexual division in our culture is the way in which women have become the repository of concern with the body, whether it be sex or health. Indeed, consciousness of the body, sexuality and health have been in almost exclusively female hands even if the higher echelons of the health professions have been occupied by men. On the surface the ease with which women have been made central in these new ideologies around health and the body might appear to be just a continuation of the ways in which women are called upon by ideologies of the fit body. In the ideologies of fitness, women have been involved with a movement for health through an already highly constructed set of assumptions about what women's bodies should or should not look like, assumptions which have, historically, operated to control and restrict women. Yet women's involvement in alternative therapies, and 'nature-based' movements, is also a slightly new configuration of an old theme. Intersecting at points with certain feminist ideas, the discourse about and for women is (at least overtly) about power and about changes to the sexist status quo.

Instead of women's involvement with the body making them slaves to fashionable ideals, it is now offered as a source of strength, albeit one which men have tried to deny. Indeed, because women's bodies have been a source of oppression, especially within conventional medicine, we are now told that women have a privileged understanding of all those natural virtues which male science and medicine have tried to suppress. In these new views, technological and scientific culture is seen as male since it is men who have had social power. Women's contact with nature is offered as the salvation to the technological madness imposed by men. Women in this new configuration have become the repository of the lost relationship with nature which modern culture has put under threat. Women have retained a secret and fragile contact with nature and the essential forces of life. Being powerless, they cannot be held responsible for the onslaught on nature from technology.

Significantly, in the context of this book, women's closeness to nature is viewed as, necessarily, a link with health and healing. After all, if nature is seen as health, and women are closer to nature, then women must have remained closer to nature's healing life force.

> Women have always been healers. They were the unlicensed doctors and anatomists of western history. They were abortionists, nurses and counsellors. They were pharmacists, cultivating healing herbs and exchanging the secrets of their uses. They were the midwives, travelling from home to home and village to village. For centuries women were doctors without degrees, barred from books and lectures, learning from each other, and passing on experience from neighbour to neighbour and mother to daughter. They were called 'wise women' by the people, witches or charlatans by the authorities. Medicine is part of our heritage as women, our history, our birthright.[2]

In this re-reading of history there emerges a secret women's culture using health practices which are gentler, safer, more in touch with people and their wants than the harsh, brutal methods of uncaring professional men; 'if anything it was the male professionals who clung to untested doctrines and ritualistic practices – and it was the women healers who represented a more humane, empirical approach to healing'.[3]

Crucial in permitting this link between women and nature is the assumption that women's bodies necessarily retain a close affinity to natural processes. And it is women's capacity to give birth which has been singled out as the function which inevitably ties her closer to nature than men. Because women produce life, they understand intuitively the life-giving forces of nature. They therefore value life more and are more humane, without the capacity for harm which men have developed. Going far beyond the much-mocked lentil-eating earth mother of the natural childbirth movement, a whole new mythological woman has emerged. Part goddess, part mother, part witch, part ancient healer, this woman is the symbol of creative and healing nature itself. Because of this women can be the hope for the future by preserving nature within culture, women that is, 'bleeding painlessly in rhythm with the moon, drawing people from their bodies, producing food from their bodies for their young, to give birth and create new life'.[4]

Certainly there would be practitioners of alternative therapies, and members of the natural childbirth movement, who would be completely horrified by being subsumed into this new version of the history of women and natural healing. Yet there are clearly correspondences in ideas about women, nature, childbirth and natural health for an informal flow of ideas to happen between them. One practitioner of alternative medicine, for instance, explained the growing popularity of alternative therapies by reference to a 'changed spirit of man'. Increasingly people wanted to take part in their own cure, to be responsible for themselves. He used as his example 'the recent case of doctors in London hospitals inducing childbirth and women resisting this. Women do not want to be manipulated, in particular during the miracle of birth.'[5] He went on to note that it was women who had been the initiators of these changed attitudes. This reference both to the natural childbirth movement and feminist politics is typical. Both are taken as political precursors of the struggle between alternative and conventional medicine. And 'the feminine' is constantly cited as symptom and hope in the struggle between modern society and nature.

Similarly, the movement for women's spirituality has been able to feed off ideas in both alternative therapies and the natural childbirth movement. Both had enough hints and correspondences in ideas about the creative and beneficial forces of nature, and in ideas about the destructiveness of male technology, to permit the transformation into a fully fledged mythology of women, nature and health. And such is the interchange between these various strands that at moments it is not so easy to separate them, as in the whole (at present predominantly American) phenomenon of feminist witches who are also practitioners of 'natural medicines' and champions of natural childbirth. Yet, as with other tendencies I have been examining in this book, there is no real reason why women's capacity to give birth and the politics surrounding that fact should necessarily be transformed into a mythology of the feminine. But a closer consideration of the way in which notions of natural childbirth have been developed by this new mythology of women and medicine seems on the contrary to show an increasing neglect of the more political issues like patients' rights and challenges to medical hierarchies.

Natural childbirth

The term 'natural childbirth' has been taken into the heart of numerous discourses on health; it signifies that nature is not yet defeated. Because the movement has challenged the medical establishment (relatively successfully) and has promoted the power of women and nature, many people have found evidence and support for their emergent views of natural health. And perhaps because the childbirth movement has made most headway in gaining general public acceptance and in challenging existing practices, it is often held up as a model of health management. Indeed, natural childbirth is often plundered as the example *par excellence* of what is wrong with existing practices and how people can return both to a more natural relation to their health and to take more personal responsibility for it. Perhaps of all the critiques of orthodox medicine, the natural childbirth movement has been the most elaborated and the most popular. And as such there are many overlaps and correspondences with the ideas in the alternative health movement.

It is more than coincidence that numerous counsellors for natural childbirth also see themselves as spokeswomen for 'natural medicines'. Both alternative therapies and the childbirth movement share a distrust of the medical establishment and an emphasis on the importance of the individual in deciding how her health is managed. 'First do no harm. It's a 2000-year-old medical principle attributed to Hippocrates, and it is the guiding philosophy behind the treatment of birthing women at The Birth Place, an alternative birth centre (ABC) in . . . California.'[6] Natural childbirth, we are told, is no longer a minority, 'hippie' ideal; everywhere individuals are seeing it as an important area where they can exercise control over their bodies. 'In the '60s and '70s, out-of-hospital birth was often stereotyped as part of the back-to-earth ideal of a dreamy counter-culture. Now, however, alternative birth centres are an increasingly popular choice among a cross section of families who feel they have a right to determine the circumstances surrounding the birth of their child.'[7]

The various elements in this quotation are important; they signal the convergence of a number of strands about women and nature and personal responsibility for health. Centrally, it articulates the sense that a fundamental and natural experience which 'belongs' to women and is specific to women has been taken out of their power. And whereas in prefeminist days this control might have been reassuring, it is now viewed as an abuse of 'rights' to her own body. Medical interventions in childbirth are now viewed as dangerously out of touch with the natural forces of the body. Medical expertise, recognized as a male preserve, is seen as threatening. And it is much more common to hear complaints about excessive profession-alism and excessive reliance on technology as an abuse of natural rights and a distortion of natural instincts than it is to hear praise for the eradication of some of the dangers and complications of childbirth. Technological sophistication is not seen as a comforting expression of humanity's control over savage and cruel nature. Instead, technical expertise, in particular technology and chemi-cals, are seen as part of *man's* destruction of nature in which women are either less culpable or indeed victims.

In these increasingly hostile, impersonal and technological surroundings, natural childbirth is seen as one of the ways in which culture can reclaim its nature. Woman's reproductive capacity means that culture cannot completely eradicate everything 'natural'. In the pessimism which inevitably accompanies views of the 'destructiveness' of the modern, women are presented as the small glimmer of hope. The creation of a healthy new life, outside the constraints of technology, will always be a witness to the great and beneficial forces of nature at the basis of all human experience. It is easy to see the correspondences with the more general views of nature which I discussed earlier. The aspect of 'nature' which is emphasized here is that of nature as creative, regenerative, and productive of new life, with women symbolic of these attributes. An advertisement for a herbal energy potion, 'Women's Longevity', aptly condenses these various meanings.

> As women undo generations of limited access, the power of creative wisdom reveals new possibilities. Working to foster compassionate intelligence in a control-hungry world takes strength and awareness. And a knowledge of how to reweave the fabric of your purpose. WOMEN'S LONGEVITY is creative energy. Sustainable. Warm. Directed. Rooted in fertile ground so health blossoms day after day. Strengthening female organs to resolve monthly problems like cramping and changeable emotions. Regenerating. Reshaping the world with sublime energy.[8]

From politics to mythology

Throughout the twentieth century, birth had increasingly been treated as a problem and pregnancy as an illness. The pregnant woman had become a patient. Doctors viewed pregnancy as a series of risks to be minimized by taking control of the birth process. This trend was greatly reinforced by the development of new technology which was supposed to reduce risks still further. The late 1940s and 1950s saw the culmination of these tendencies, with a massive move in favour of hospital births, finally consolidating the professionalization of health care for pregnant women. The vision of childbirth in the late 1950s is of a woman supine on the delivery table with her feet in stirrups and her pubic hair shaved. She is attended by masked strangers while her excluded partner anxiously prowls the corridors. The medical profession justified these practices by reference to the dramatic decrease in perinatal mortality, although it may well be that with improved hygiene alone the numbers of infant deaths would have dropped. It is hard to resist speculation that, mixed with concern for women's and children's safety, was a male abhorrence of women's bodily functions and a desire to sanitize and control them. After all, to give birth lying down is the worst and most painful position for women but is altogether less threatening and more convenient for the male doctor.

Ideas about a more 'natural childbirth' were hardly new. In *Natural Childbirth*, published in 1933, Grantly Dick Read promoted relaxation techniques as a natural way of overcoming fear and pain. But his ideas were viewed with outright hostility by the medical establishment and had only limited circulation. In the late 1950s, however, groups of women who used his ideas to challenge the prevailing medical orthodoxy began to emerge and the National Childbirth Trust was formed. Although these women hoped to reduce medical intervention, they made little criticism of existing hospital practices. It was the writings of Frederick Leboyer which transformed the situation, and since the 1960s, a version of his ideas has come to dominate (middle-class) beliefs about childbirth. Leboyer stressed that current methods of childbirth were positively inhuman and brutal towards the child, rendering birth traumatic rather than joyful. He argued that Western culture refused to recognize that a child might be conscious of the process of birth itself. Westerners had ceased to see 'this new being in its separate reality'. Instead everyone involved in the birth congratulated each other, leaving the newborn child to experience a trauma so deep that it will be felt in his or her personality for the rest of their life.

As with many of the ideas in circulation in the 1960s, the seeds were there for germination into the fully fledged criticism of medicine characteristic of the 1980s. Leboyer stressed women's own natural instinctive knowledge as well as emphasizing the importance of heightened experience and 'consciousness'. Consciousness, in fact, is central to Leboyer's ideas but it is the consciousness of the infant. He is little interested in the experience of the mother. Indeed, in keeping with his psychoanalytic, and particularly Kleinian bent, it is easy to form the impression that the hostile struggle between mother and child is one of the factors which makes birth so traumatic for the child. In his view conventional birth practices exacerbate the emotions of that struggle. It was only later that Leboyer's ideas were joined with criticisms of women's experience of birth to produce a critique of childbirth more from the women's point of view. In the 1970s there was a mounting awareness that an experience which is central and specific to women had been taken out of their hands. Women began to feel cheated of responsibility.

This convergence of Leboyer's ideas of conscious childbirth with a move for women to gain far greater control in the experience of birth created the conditions for the emergence of the natural childbirth movement. Its main elements were, and remain, an emphasis on heightened consciousness of the experience of birth for both mother and baby, greater autonomy of women from the medical profession to determine the condition and practices of giving birth, and a break with the 'passive' poses by which women were previously encouraged to give birth. Yet there is clearly tension over whether these ideas are to be appropriated into some new mythology about the suppression of women's power, or whether the issue is political, about current attitudes towards women in the health services. For many women the natural childbirth movement is primarily a political movement albeit a quiet one. For the issue is about medical hierarchies in which men have power, about attitudes of health service professionals, and about the way in which women have been infantilized and rendered invalids in what ought to be an empowering experience. For an activist like Sheila Kitzinger the movement has political implications for the reorganization of the health services, a reorganization which would challenge the medical hierarchy, involve greater recognition of the midwife's status, and give greater responsibility to women to decide where and how they wish to give birth.

But even though the issues are political for many of the activists, it is also a movement which at certain moments drinks deeply from the fountain of beliefs and attitudes about what is natural and healthy for the body and what is wrong with the existing technological approach to medicine. First, in spite of the caution of some writers, many cheerfully uphold the idea that we can know what a natural childbirth might be. This knowledge is usually based on hazy ideas about so-called 'primitive' people on the one hand and women's 'deep instinctive knowledge' in childbirth on the other. Basing her ideas on a book, *Labour among Primitive Peoples*, written in the late nineteenth century, Janet Balaskas the Active Birth campaigner tells us that 'primitive tribes have adopted various birth positions through customs of their tribe, but more importantly by their instinct . . . Women of different tribes squat, kneel, stand, incline, sit or lie on the belly; so, too, do they vary their position in various stages of labour and difficult labours.'[9]

As I have argued earlier in connection with these views about 'natural' knowledge, any reference to what primitive people do must be regarded as highly suspect. Indeed Balaskas's own quotation gives away the problem. If groups of people are influenced by 'customs' then, by definition, the act does not belong to nature but to culture, however basic and fundamental to all life and creatures the act of giving birth is. So, of course, is the act of going to the toilet, but how and where we choose to do it is very much the product of customs, conventions, taboos, religious disgust, etc. To say that we are all born, eat, shit and die, and that most of us have sex and reproduce, tells us very little about nature. All societies, however simple or non-technical they may appear, actually have complex regulations around birth, eating, shitting and sex. And it really is impossible to use non-European societies as examples of the natural.

Not all ideas about women's instinctual knowledge rely on dubious observations of 'primitive' women. Many define this instinctive knowledge as an internal force, known only when inhibitions and social expectations are removed, and which women can re-find by working on and focusing on the moment of birth. An American active birth centre, for example, offers to help women 'discover their instinctive potential for giving birth and to develop ease in the upright and supported postures natural to labour and birth.'[10] The natural force which attracts the attention of the alternative health movement is a force found again, internally, in the individual. 'Naturebirth is consciousbirth. To be conscious of birth we need to be conscious in pregnancy; we need to know as much as possible about our bodies, our minds and how they function together, both during the time the baby is forming in the womb and in the powerful movements and sensations during labour.'[11]

Again, there are many people in the natural childbirth movement who distance themselves from any simplistic idea of women's instinctual knowledge. Michel Odent, for example, tries to drive a fine and not always clear line between himself and exponents of women's instinctive knowledge. He uses the term 'instinctual' to describe 'this shift to a deeper level of consciousness during labour' but is careful to qualify it. He denies that he means 'a return to an animal state'. Nor, he says, does he wish to fall into the age-old trap of using the term instinct for women which is then used against them to tell them how they should 'instinctively' feel about motherhood, babies, sex and so on. He continues, however,

> there is nothing shameful or sexist in recognizing that instinct plays a part in our behaviours, especially those which exist at the intersection of nature and culture, such as lovemaking, labour, or the newborn's search for the mother's nipple. People can and do benefit enormously from rediscovering and exploiting to the fullest their instinctive potential on these occasions.[12]

Sheila Kitzinger is even more careful not to fall into any simple and reductionist idea that 'natural childbirth' is all about expressing the primitive and the instinctual,

> When Michel says we must strip away the cultural excrescences of birth in order to rediscover our instinctual selves, he is not advocating any simple return to some ideal of the primitive. In fact he has not discarded culture. He has taken the institutional artefacts of our culture and adapted them to meet women's instinctual needs in childbirth. He works, for example, in a hospital setting not at home, and anticipates that professionals with special skills will take part in the birth. The lights that are dimmed, the tape recorder with music if a woman wants it during labour, the pool used for relaxation – all these are the products of industrial organisation and modern civilisation.[13]

Kitzinger's comments certainly seem to correspond with my own experiences. Both the births I have experienced were what some people might call 'natural', one at hospital and one at home. Yet in spite of the fact that these were drug-free, non-interventionist births, I was conscious of the availability of all sorts of medical resources if anything was to go wrong.

But careful qualifications like Kitzinger's belong largely to those involved in the *politics* of childbirth and those with close links with the feminist issues raised by it all. They understand all too well that the association of women with the instincts and with nature has been one of the crucial ways in which women's oppression has been justified. In the past, as with Grantly Dick Read's exhortations, the association was one which emphasized women's natural destiny for motherhood, such a great spiritual calling, they told us, that women could not possibly and reasonably seek for any other satisfactions outside the home and their children. The qualifications point to an understanding that the directly political element of the natural childbirth movement is liable to be submerged in attempts to plunder the movement for what it can tell us about the great forces of nature at work in women's bodies.

Whereas a writer like Kitzinger is anxious that her ideas have wide political implications for the management of the health services and the way in which women in particular are treated by those services, other writers are far more keen to make birth a symbol for a whole series of beliefs about nature, the body, health and women. It is far commoner to find that the experience of birth has been appropriated as the expression of a lost instinctual force. Increasingly the issues around natural childbirth have been taken as emblematic of the modern mismanagement of health. Increasingly, too, the explanation for this management is given in terms of rather bowdlerized versions of feminist history. In this history, women's 'alienation' from their natural and healthy instincts during birth is seen as symptomatic of the whole history of the alienation of us all from our own healthy bodily impulses. Thus, increasingly, the politics involved in the natural childbirth movement have been at risk from this need to claim the process of giving birth, and women's special role in this, as the symbol of natural health and the symbol of resistance to male technology.

Midwives and 'pre-patriarchal' healers

There are some feminist critics who see the progressive medicalization of childbirth as part of the general way in which women were divested of power in the community. They see the way in which female midwives were displaced as symptomatic of the struggle between health, nature and women on one side and science, ill health and men on the other. It is certainly the case that as the profession of doctor became increasingly respectable throughout the eighteenth century, women involved in health were displaced from their various roles in the community. Midwives were a particular target for this struggle between 'traditional' methods of health care and new 'scientific' medicine. Doctors saw themselves as the representatives of science dispelling the miasma of tradition,

superstition and religious confusion which they thought characterized the activities of the local healers, herbalists and midwives.
Women were singled out as a major force of reaction, locked in
their traditional ways, refusing the knowledge of modern medicine
in preference to 'folkloric remedies' even when it meant jeopardiz-
ing their patients. Women were represented as bearers of tradition,
superstition, and nature, which in combination were seen by the
medical establishment as the forces of ignorance and regression.
George Crabbe's *Parish Register* of 1807 recorded how 'The
young doctor . . . sneered at the midwife as "nature's slave" who
trusted only to luck, and in emergencies to prayer, while he with
his "skill" and "courage" took pleasure in bending nature to his
will.'[14]

It is difficult to ascertain exactly what was going on in midwifery
before the medical profession began to intervene. Clearly, in a
struggle over who was to control the area of childbirth, the medical
profession had much to gain in representing women as dangerously
driven by superstitious beliefs. And it is also clear that the
designation of women as simple, close to nature and therefore
prone to ignorant superstitions was, at least in part, a prejudice of
the eighteenth century – the period when doctors really began to
challenge the traditional methods of delivering babies. Both these
facts suggest that feminists are right to be suspicious when
orthodox medical history represents the displacement of midwives
as dispelling the mists of ignorance, superstition and magic.
Research into the area of midwifery indicates that, for the most
part, the women responsible for delivering babies even in the
Middle Ages used 'a combination of conventional techniques,
"earthly medicine" and usually only as a last resort, appeals to the
saints and supernatural forces in the form of amulets, incantations
and so forth'.[15] It seems reasonably certain that midwifery was
misrepresented by doctors mainly because it was such a contested
area. Midwifery was at the point of intersection of a number of
conflicts, mainly the conflict between the extension of medical
control over the body in the form of the profession of doctoring and
the development of hospitals, and the conflict between men and
women generated by the establishment of the professional classes
as powerful and almost exclusively male.

However, many sympathizers with the idea that midwifery has

been sadly misrepresented have gone a good deal further than my cautious remarks. They believe that from the history of the struggle over midwifery, we can read off a whole alternative history of women's relation to the management of health. Some supporters of alternative methods of healing have turned to this history of women's relationship to the medical profession to elaborate a model of the suppression of feminine knowledge of the body, health and healing. There is a forceful, 'feminist' strand which claims that the practice of natural medicines, like herbalism, was always known to women healers and midwives. Indeed, these feminists claim that what the medical profession and the church viewed as magic and superstition was in fact the use of natural medicine. According to this history, the power which these skills gave women was only lost when men actively began to control medicine and punish women for their different knowledge. These accounts rely on the hypothesis of a 'pre-patriarchal' era (and a concomitant vision of a post-patriarchal era) where women and their natural and instinctual knowledge were revered.

> Healing has not always operated on the model of the externally produced 'cure' that informs contemporary medicine . . . Pre-patriarchal cultures were in their totality, healing experiences, and women were essential contributors to this state. They were the original healers, the midwives, herbalists, myth-makers, spiritual guides, psychic and death guides.[16]

In this alternative account, the values of the eighteenth-century critics of the midwives have simply been inverted. There is an acceptance that women are close to nature; there is an acceptance that midwifery practices were based on traditional medicines, and 'superstitious' practices. But now, armed with the alternative therapies' criticisms of orthodox medicine, these have been turned into positive attributes. Indeed the activities, potions and remedies offered by the early midwives and herbalists have been (theoretically at least) elevated into superior forms of medicine. This inversion is going a good deal further than claims that the history of midwifery (including its contemporary history) is about the struggle over how competent women were allowed to be, and their resistance to attempts to change their status. Instead, the whole history of midwifery and the issues raised by non-medicalized (or natural) childbirth have been taken up as a vital struggle between the natural, powerful and creative forces of women opposed to the destructive, negative powers of men and professionalism. Natural childbirth in these accounts has become a symbol of women's eternal closeness with nature, and midwifery a symbol of women's knowledge of the healing arts which corresponds to this instinctive knowledge of nature.

It probably needs little reiteration that this alternative version of midwifery and natural childbirth is as distorted as the 'male' accounts which it seeks to replace. Nature all too tangibly cannot be relied upon to provide straightforward, uncomplicated and safe births. And the obstetric practices preceding hospitalized births clearly claimed as many casualties as the practices which followed. Again one has to stress what a selective view of nature this is. In *A History of Women's Bodies*, Edward Shorter produces a most horrific account of some of the things that did go wrong with women's bodies in childbirth, even as recently as the last century. He chronicles rampant child-bed fever, ruptured uteruses, women whose wombs had inverted and dangled between their legs, and women whose urine and faeces flowed interchangeably between the various orifices, so damaged had they been in the process of childbirth. Perhaps Shorter is a little extreme in his vision but his account is salutary. In order that nature can be perceived as ever beneficial, creative and kind one has to assume a degree of sanitation and hygiene. In this account we have to assume a nature which is already controlled and sanitized before it is given its free expression.

From midwifery to the eco-witches

This interpretation of midwifery typifies the way in which there is an attempt to attribute to women (both now and historically) a power derived from nature. Thus the whole history of midwifery and childbirth is conceived of as a struggle between men (representing culture, rationality and technology) and women (representing the life forces, nature, and very often the supernatural). And a new feminist tendency concerned with Women's Spirituality has derived its theory and rationale from this account of women's power and the attempt to suppress it. The movement is somewhat paradoxically named since the power which is attributed to woman is based on her closeness to nature. But it is precisely this closeness which is supposed to feed women's spirituality. By a similar equation this movement also gives a home to women and the supernatural; it is the place where you are most likely to find the feminist Tarot readers and feminist witches. The argument runs that when intellect, rationality and materialism were valued, then the knowledge which came from nature was interpreted as superstition and ignorance. Thus the supernatural was really only intuitive 'natural' understanding that was devalued by men.

In this rehabilitation of the supernatural, the witch has become a crucial symbol. Not only is the witch now viewed as a sort of proto-feminist early homoeopath, but there has also been the literal emergence of a popular witchcraft movement. The rehabilitation of the witch requires this paradoxical association of women both with nature and the *super*natural; all the earlier sexist assumptions about women have been embraced and inverted into positive features. Yes, it is said, women are closer to natural forces; yes, women have always used traditional, natural medicines, which copy the healing actions of nature itself; and yes, women do appeal to supernatural and magic forces. But to be close to nature is now viewed as good and proper – after all, look at the mess men have made. To use natural medicines is good – they are safe and work in harmony with nature. And as for superstition, that is only men's rationalist way of dismissing women's intuitive knowledge of how things connect together, how things work, and how things will turn out.

The oldest and wisest among us can read disorder. From dreams or the utterances of madness, the chance cracks on a tortoise shell, the fortunate shapes of leaves of tea, the fateful arrangement of cards, we can tell things. And some of us can heal. We can read bodies with our hands, read the earth, find water, trace gravity's path. We know what grows and how to balance one thing against another.[17]

In this history it was only the emergence of male-dominated medicine which drove these women away from their traditional role.

Throughout the pre-patriarchal era, some women have always fought to participate in their own health care, to protect the ancient healing ways, and to affirm their strength and wholeness. While most women succumbed to political, cultural and economic pressures to fulfil the narrowly defined roles of mother, wife and nurse in patriarchal culture, other women – the wise women – harked back to the strong female models of pre-patriarchal days. They were the healers, herbalists, midwives and psychics, maintaining connection to the magic and mystery of life and to the forces of natural, healing ways.[18]

In fact, the very women who appealed to natural forces and intuition were precisely those who were persecuted as witches, since what the Church took to be the workings of the Devil was often the workings of nature. 'Many of us who practised these arts were put on trial . . . They would have had all of us perish and most of us did. But some kept on. Because this is the power of such things as we know – we kept flying through the night, we kept up our deviling, our dancing, we were still familiar with the animals though we were threatened with fire and though we were almost to a woman burned.'[19] In one breathless act, witch persecution is reduced to one cause: the struggle between men and women, embodied in the struggle between traditional, folkloric, or superstitious beliefs and the rationalism of the Church and the medical profession.

This view of witchcraft has about as much historical validity as the image of the witch in a Walt Disney cartoon. But it has laid the foundations for a whole new variation of contemporary 'feminist' witchcraft. Not only is the witch the repository of ancient knowledges about natural medicines, she is also the repository of ancient, pre-Christian, pre-patriarchal values, the values of paganism and nature worship. Different aspects of the witch are emphasized by different groups. On the one hand is the witch who retains elements of her popular 'wicked' connotations. She is a trifle diabolic and distinctly subversive, not evil, you understand, because it is the values of the dominant culture which are wrong.

Witches were the first Friendly heads and Dealers, the first birth-control practitioners and abortionists, the first alchemists (turn dross into gold and you devalue the whole idea of money).

They bowed to no man, being the living remnant of the oldest culture of all-one in which men and women were equal sharers in a truly co-operative society before the death-dealing sexual, economic and spiritual oppression of the Imperialist Phallic Society took over and began to destroy nature and human society.[20]

On the other hand there is the newly sanitized witch, cleaned of any odour of black magic, evil or Satanism. She may still carry connotations of sexuality but even these are distinctly wholesome. This witch is also an inheritor of ancient knowledges but these are the natural knowledges of the earth. This is the witch who is the worshipper of the Goddess, a devotee of paganism, as the ancient universal religion of Goddess and Earth worship. 'Today the revival of interest in occult beliefs and practices is firmly centred in the return to the Goddess – the veneration of the Universal Feminine Principle which has for so long been neglected in our society.'[21] This witch is very firmly and unmistakably on the side of Good. She stands for collectivism, egalitarianism, harmony with nature, opposition to all attempts to despoil and destroy nature. She is a helper, healer and carer. Her 'magic' is simply a reflection of ancient knowledges of nature, handed down in the heritage of witchcraft, a power for good.

Love for Life in all its forms is the basic ethic of Witchcraft. Witches are bound to honour and respect all living things, and to serve the life force. While the Craft recognizes that life feeds on life and that we must kill in order to survive, life is never taken needlessly, never squandered or wasted. Serving the life force means working to preserve the diversity of natural life, to prevent the poisoning of the environment and the destruction of the species.[22]

This is the new Eco-Witch, upholder of the principles of life and nature, and therefore inevitably the values I outlined in Chapter 1 – the life-giving, healing forces of nature. And in perhaps an even more striking area of correspondence with ideas we have been discussing elsewhere in this book, this witch has a holistic consciousness. She sees the connections between things (hence her intuition and magic) and she seeks always to work in harmony with nature and to restore balance.

The harmonious balance of plant/animal/divine awareness is not automatic; it must constantly be renewed, and this is the true function of craft rituals. Inner work, spiritual work, is most effective when it proceeds hand in hand with outer work. Meditation on the balance of nature might be considered a spiritual act in Witchcraft, but not as much as would cleaning up garbage left at a campsite or marching to protest an unsafe nuclear plant.[23]

Here, the religion of the Goddess is the religion of an original holism, before patriarchy and male technology fragmented our relation with nature and our perceptions of ourselves.

In this account, the religious and rationalist beliefs of Western science are both explained as fragmentation and estrangement of the self from nature. Goddess worship, witchcraft and paganism on the contrary are seen as the principles of immanence and holism.

Immanence, expressed in the Goddess, dispels the roots of estrangement. Good, true value, is not found in some heaven, some abstract other world, but in female bodies and their offspring, in nature and the world. Nature is seen as having its own, inherent order, of which human beings are part.[24]

Even the rituals of witchcraft are translated into the prayers celebrating the holism within things which has been so threatened by rationalist society.

Her breath is still. The night is still. The forces of Life wait expectantly and suddenly light returns to flood the room and the Priestess of the Moon cries out to the Primordial Mother, to whom she was bequeathed before the Dawn of Time. The mother answers with the heartbreak of a thousand million lives and acknowledges the Child. They fuse and are one, the cycle is complete, and the Priestess of the Moon is assured . . . And the work of the Goddess will continue though to most her Name is unknown; through the one will the knowledge proceed and the Earth will flourish. And she cries to the Ancient Power a renewal of her oath that all things will be done and in the Mother's name.[25]

I hardly know where to start in discussing these beliefs, so riddled are they with incorrect and problematic assumptions.

Most overwhelming is the staggering reduction of the complex history of witchcraft to the struggle between masculine and feminine values. One version of this, in circulation among American feminists, is the insistence that the persecution of witches was the persecution of the female principles of healing and community health care by the two-fold forces of Church and medicine. Obviously the fact that most witches who were burned were female is not irrelevant, although it is a fact often overlooked by male historians. Undoubtedly, the way in which women were perceived and treated had a great deal to do with why they became the victims of a hysterical persecution. And it is possible that, in selecting various local women to be named as witches, factors such as their use of non-Christian, folkloric remedies and unorthodox sexual behaviour played a part. Nevertheless this does not translate into a suppression of ancient feminine values. Indeed the evidence there is about the women herbalists was that they were highly qualified professionals who took their craft extremely seriously as a science and regarded themselves in an almost professional light.

As far as there is any agreement about the persecution of witches (in an area of research which has produced wildly divergent explanations) two factors seem crucial. One is that the practice of extracting confessions by and about witches itself generated more and more witches. The practice was self-enlarging; each conviction led to others, generating a proliferation of named witches and trials. Secondly, changes within religious discourse, either in the form of conflict between two religions or in the form of changes in the beliefs of the dominant religion seem to have been crucial in feeding the hysteria amongst the local population, necessary to sustain the hysteria and persecution. Keith Thomas in *Religion and the Decline of Magic* offers a highly plausible account of the development of witchcraft in England. He suggests that the playing down of ritual and magic in the new Protestant religions left villages feeling unprotected and powerless in the face of 'the workings of the devil'.

Thomas speculates that these workings of the devil probably included unaccountable sexual frenzy or appetite, rebellion against the Church and authorities, blasphemy, and unexplained and uncontrollable illness. The medieval Church had been happy to exorcize the Devil, leaving the individual in question both absolved and faultless. After all, if the devil took possession of an individual, it was not a problem of his or her own sin. Reformation doctrine, on the other hand, prohibited all uses of 'magic' and insisted that the only way to overcome the workings of the devil was through fasting and prayer, an internal struggle against sin – poor comfort to those who were at the rough end of the injustices and vicissitudes which life could deal. Such changes made fertile ground for the projection of fears of diabolic influence on to the outside, on to the image of the woman in a secret pact with the Devil and responsible for the ills of a community.

None of this is to deny the significance of the fact that it was women who were the focus of fears of the diabolic and magic. But it is to suggest that it would be quite wrong to ignore the explicit components of witch persecution. For those involved in the trials and for the locals who called for the persecutions (including numerous women) there was little question that what was at stake were issues of the diabolic, and the use of magic to do harm. It seems unlikely that local women could have turned so whole-heartedly against the traditional healers and proto-herbalists if they were indeed perceived as the true bringers of hope, healing and health into the community. The persecution of witches clearly entailed the persecution of women by men and the use of this persecution to further certain social changes including, impor-tantly, appropriation of property. But this does not necessarily mean that the women who were persecuted were the inheritors of a secret knowledge and defenders of the essential feminine principles.

This leads to the second dubious assumption about witches. There is an equally common belief that not only were the persecuted witches the innocent healers and herbalists but that many of them may well have been real witches, that is, pagans or nature worshippers. Yet there is no real evidence of a continuous unbroken tradition of covens which upheld paganism in the face of all attempts to obliterate it (although of course witches would insist that the essence of witchcraft is its secret nature). Nor is there any evidence of pockets of paganism lingering on through Europe. However there is a great deal of evidence that the *idea* of an original paganism as the universal and first religion was a 'literary' creation belonging to the turn of the century. That period was the great period of universalizing explanations about religion, about marriage, and about sexual customs, explanations which always tried to establish that there was 'An Original Form' from which all other customs derived. Thus many folkloric customs came to be viewed as residues of pagan culture. Witchcraft, it was suggested, had not been assimilated to Christianity; it preserved the elements of the original religion, paganism. It seems to have been in the 1930s that this theory received its particularly naturist gloss; witchcraft then acquired a heritage as being a religion, a nature religion, *the* nature religion in which worship of the Goddess (in a number of different forms) was seen as worship of the earth.

Contemporary feminist witches have taken on board this history of the witch in spite of its lack of intellectual credibility. And the contemporary elevation of natural principles as feminine principles is as dubious now as it was in that earlier period. For one thing the equation is tautologous. The equation requires that nature is viewed in the ways I outlined in Chapter 1 (beneficial, healing, and gentle) and everything in nature which contradicts this has to be disregarded. Similarly 'femininity' has to have the same qualities. There is no place here for regarding the feminine as angry, aggressive and destructive. Although many contemporary witches appear to 'value' women's strength and self-assertion, it is entirely in terms of being strong in the face of hardship or victimization. Nowhere in this discourse is the possibility that all human beings (both males and females) are born with aggressive and destructive impulses or that both sexes can love and hate. In other words, it is an equation based on two ideological constructs, that of nature and that of the feminine.

Most dubious in the current link drawn between the feminine and natural principles is the concomitant belief that the feminine stands for everything that is humane, egalitarian and progressive. Recent views of the feminine suggest that now women have the possibility of economic and social autonomy from men, they will be able to give expression to their essentially 'compassionate' nature which connects with respect for the natural order. Much of the support for women's peace camps like Greenham has been lent precisely in these terms. In this new configuration of feminism and alternative health, there is an insistence that the 'feminine' (if it can be re-appropriated from its negative associations under patriarchy) is at the basis of a new politics and therefore the hope for the planet's future. It is a politics based on a 'new value system, a new ethic: the human body'. And from this new ethic will emerge a natural predisposition to 'gentle' medicines, a concern for nutrition, a predisposition towards pacifism, an understanding of healing and a commitment to ecological politics.

In this ethic of the human body, woman's capacity to give birth is a crucial determinant in her natural predisposition towards alternative medicine and eco-politics. A combination of the direct experience of the creative and beneficial forces of nature with maternal altruism leads her inevitably towards caring about plants, animals, the environment and other human beings.

> Biology for sure is destiny . . . as women we are what the patriarchy has labelled us: vessels, containers, receptacles, carriers, shelters, houses, nurturers, incubators, holders, enfolders, listeners. We are built to receive. We are also built to give, but even our giving is in our own mode. Instead of probing and invading, our natural giving takes the path of wrapping around the givee, of being available to her/him, without insisting; our giving is a presence, an offering, an opening, a surrounding, a listening, a vulnerability, a trust. At the very most our giving takes the form of a push toward freedom for the givee, as in the act of giving birth.[26]

Quite apart from the fact that I have immense difficulty in recognizing myself in that account of femininity, a number of factors should encourage caution in the face of such glowing accounts of female altruism extending endlessly from one's own child, to others, to the Earth and to nature itself. For one thing history is far from consoling on this one. Perhaps women have been instrumental in contemporary ecological politics, and in terms of *direct* culpability women do seem less responsible than men for some of the atrocities committed, atrocities against fellow human beings, against animals and against the environment. But such an observation is neither wholly true nor does it necessarily require that we construct a mythology with women more in touch with essential life forces. While women may not have been powerful (which renders them perhaps less culpable) they have nevertheless been *complicit*.

It might be regarded as treasonous to raise such issues, but the fact is that women have not only stood by but have also supported some of the worst atrocities in human history. There is as much evidence of men's resistance to injustice, oppression, repression, and tyranny as there is evidence of women's. And what is particularly galling from the point of view of the essential and good feminine, is that the support given to men who abuse power has more often than not been lent precisely in the name of what it is 'right' for woman to do. Thus, complicity with husbands, bosses and employers, with authoritarian leaders and even fascist dictators is often recruited from women by appeals to the essential feminine, that is, concern with the world of childbirth, childcare and care of the domestic. Some argue that women's complicity is directly attributable to the fact that women are still oppressed by men and cannot therefore express their true nature. But only a brief glance at contemporary Britain must give pause for thought. While women are clearly still discriminated against and oppressed in many ways, nevertheless, the possibilities for independence from men do exist. Yet here women constitute a significant political factor in supporting the political philosophy of Conservatism which is the antithesis of everything the Essential Feminine is supposed to represent. In short, factors like class seem also to determine how individual women will feel about their fellow mortals.

Secondly, and connected, there is no evidence that the capacity to, or the experience of, giving birth necessarily predisposes women in a more progressive direction. It is certainly true that many women describe an extreme emotional vulnerability after childbirth, where they find any information about suffering and death impossibly hard to bear. These are the emotions so unhelpfully described as the 'baby blues', blamed on the ever-culpable hormones. But this excess of feeling probably has quite other roots, roots in the fact that for the period around birth normal defences are down and all the participants feel extremely close to the magnificence and frailty of human life. At this time women do at least have the *potential* for an instantaneous non-individualistic empathy with others.

But more often than not, this sensitivity to the frailty and value of life has been mobilized by reactionary ideologies like the patriarchal religions of which women have been such enthusiastic supporters. Christianity certainly celebrated this altruistic state of motherhood but made it subordinate to a higher mission, that of sacrifice to her son and submission to paternal power. Contrary to the idea of women connected to all, equally, this image is more often at the basis of woman's devotion to her *own* child, and sometimes her own nation, or the nation's children. The image just as often feeds the idea of woman oblivious to others and to politics and the outside world. This is the woman whose concern for humanity is expressed only through her devotion to her own family. Such is the fertile ground in which extreme right-wing politics take hold, just as much as ecologically aware politics. Any generalized empathy which women might feel seems to have been all too easily mobilized into individualistic directions. And what is more, altruism and respect for the value of life have never 'belonged' to women. Men who have witnessed births or been close to people dying have described the same sensitivity to others; whether that translates into an egalitarian and compassionate politics seems to depend on a whole series of other factors.

Conclusions

Although the link drawn between the female body and progressive politics is historically dubious, the desire to develop this new ethics of the human body strikes me as highly problematic. To make women's orifices and organs the source of reverence is really not much of an improvement on making them the source of revulsion (which is the oppression which women have suffered in traditional patriarchal cultures and religions). The issue is not really whether women's genitals are revered or reviled, but the fact that women by virtue of their bodies are rendered symbols. Far from being a new ethic, this is the time-honoured way in which women have always been treated. When any group (whether it be sexual or ethnic) becomes a symbol, the individuals in that group will be defined from outside and suffer from that identity. They acquire, regardless of their numerical status, the status of a minority; their characteristics are decided by other's fantasies and projections not by anything which any individual might want to offer of her or himself. What is presupposed in this symbol is a normal female body, geared up towards reproduction (even if she should choose not to reproduce) and a whole series of normal emotions which are supposed to follow from having that body. What gradually disappears is the possibility of individual variations and divergences. What becomes overwhelmingly important is a person's identity with a group, an identity valued far more than divergence and deviation.

To attribute essential characteristics to a person along with her genitals is hardly a *new* ethic of the human body. It is the age-old ethic by which women have been rendered the defined and excluded minority. No attempt to invert the values and turn women into Godheads will be able to break out of that. In this new elevation of the body and instinctual knowledge, we can see all the classic hallmarks of what is happening to notions of the body and health elsewhere. Instead of a politics directed at transforming the treatment of the patient and in particular the medical conception of women, we have the emergence of a philosophy, a philosophy of nature and feminine values. While this philosophy might offer itself as political, that is, attempting to transform the status of women by unconventional means, it in fact basks in all the forms by which women have traditionally been oppressed. This new religion of the body is not part of a revolutionary consciousness, but part of the general drift into making health and the body a philosophical, moral and religious concern rather than a political one.

Notes

1 Charlene Spretnak, *The Politics of Women's Spirituality*.
2 Barbara Ehrenreich and Deirdre English, *Witches, Midwives and Nurses*.
3 ibid.
4 Introduction to Spretnak, op. cit.
5 Interview at the Institute for Complementary Medicine.
6 'Active Birth Centres' in *East/West* magazine, Jan. 1987.
7 ibid.
8 Advertisement for Women's Longevity, herbal energy potion.
9 Janet Balaskas, *Active Birth*.
10 'Active Birth Centres', op. cit.

11 Danae Brook, *Naturebirth*.

12 Michel Odent, *Birth Reborn*.

13 Sheila Kitzinger, Introduction to *Birth Reborn*, op. cit.

14 Quoted by Jean Donnison in *Midwives and Medical Men*, Heinemann Publications, 1977.

15 Peter Biller, 'Childbirth in the Middle Ages', *History Today*, August 1986.

16 Chellis Glendinning, 'The Healing Powers of Women' in Spretnak, op. cit.

17 Susan Griffin, *Woman and Nature*.

18 Glendinning, op. cit.

19 Griffin, op. cit.

20 W.I.T.C.H., 'Spooking the Patriarchy', in Spretnak, op. cit.

21 Starhawk, 'Witchcraft as Goddess Religion', in Spretnak, op. cit.

22 ibid.

23 ibid.

24 Starhawk, 'Consciousness, Politics, Magic', in Spretnak, op. cit.

25 Ly Warren-Clarke, *The Way of the Goddess: A Manual for Wiccan Initiation*.

26 Spretnak, op. cit.

7 Aids – the Symptomatic Disease *par excellence*

Aids is a disease without its 'own' symptoms. It is usually first recognized by the symptoms of other associated illnesses. Rather than a positive identification of Aids, tests can only reveal the presence or absence of antibodies to the virus and these 'do not indicate whether or not a person has or will ever develop Aids'.[1] In the absence of any positive proof or definite symptoms, instead there's a list of common opportunistic infections, including a distinctive kind of pneumonia or various fungal infections, which are used as 'indicators of Aids'.[2] It is perhaps cruelly pertinent then that this disease without its own symptoms should itself be a symptom *par excellence*. The responses to, and struggles over, Aids are in some very precise way, symptoms of the attitudes towards illness, well-being and society which I have been discussing in this book.

Although illness and death will always be with us, different diseases are invested with symbolic significance at different moments of history, becoming metaphors for prevailing preoccupations around the body, health, disease, and even the state of society. They acquire far more significance for the population in general than do other illnesses of the time. Susan Sontag has suggested that there was a general belief in the nineteenth century that TB was a disease of passion. 'Fever in TB was a sign of an inward burning: the tubercular is someone "consumed" by ardour, that ardour leading to the dissolution of the body.'[3] Even for its victims, TB came to symbolize a certain kind of romantic wasting, becoming a metaphor for a particular kind of poetic suffering characteristic of certain sensitive people. Although TB also carried moralistic overtones that the sufferer lacked 'vitality', and was weak or lacking in the will to live, it also had a romantic glamour, implying someone whose soul and spirituality were too sensitive for ordinary life.

No such glamour attaches to Aids, yet it is no less of a symbolic disease. In the current responses to Aids we can detect all the major themes, and major divisions over the meanings of health and illness, which this book is investigating. Because it is an illness which appears to challenge fundamentally the competence of modern medicine, Aids has come to join cancer as a disease where alternative philosophies of health and illness can flourish. Because Aids and immunity are inseparable concepts, the illness is at the front line in struggles over how to understand disease and the natural health of the body. Crucially, Aids pinpoints the whole conflict over the status of the viral disease versus the overall health of the host. But in many other ways too, Aids seems to symbolize some of the more general contemporary shifts around the body and health. Not only does Aids appear to undermine the attitudes of conventional medicine, but it also foregrounds the way in which morality and medicine have enmeshed – and this is true for much of the commentary about Aids, whether it comes from sexual conservatives or exponents of radical changes in life style. And because Aids raises issues about both sex *and* health, it shows clearly how many of the questions of morality previously rooted in attitudes towards sex have shifted to health.

The virus and immunity

How significant it is that the late twentieth century should be locked in struggle with a horrific 'disease' which so exactly encapsulates the dilemmas of, and challenges to, modern medical knowledge of the body. When Aids emerged conventional medicine was still able to base its claims for superiority over any alternative methods on its triumphant control of epidemic illnesses. Although conventional medicine had little success with many chronic and degenerative illnesses, when it comes to contagious epidemics there could be a justifiable boast that almost all were under control. And the explanation for these successes was largely in terms of scientific knowledge of bacteria and viruses and the efficacy of antibiotics and vaccines. Yet here was an entirely new illness and apparently pursuing the course of an epidemic illness.

Aids has threatened our sense of medical security. After all, the age of transmissible, lethal infections was deemed long past in the Western world. Ours was the chronic disease – heart disease and cancers which principally strike late in life. Communicability – epidemics of infectious diseases – had receded in public memory.[4]

Even more serious for the medical establishment has been the fact that Aids also appeared to challenge many previous assumptions about the workings of viruses and the role of medicine. When the phenomenon of Aids was first recognized in the late 1970s it appeared to medical researchers to defy previous medical knowledge on two fronts, both about the *nature* of the virus and about the *behaviour* of an epidemic illness. Previous understanding of the nature of the virus had been partly dependent on the activities of the immune system against the virus. Virus and antibody were like the back and the front of the same piece of paper. And medicine was seen as in alliance with the antibody against the enemy virus. But what appeared to happen with Aids was not that a harmful virus entered the body and then began attacking the healthy cells, either defeating the body or itself being destroyed by the body's immune system. Instead, here was an illness which appeared to trick the body's defences; something was going on which caused the healthy antibodies in the body to turn against themselves. For conventional medicine the problem was acute: what should researchers make of a virus which settled in the cells whose very function was to destroy elements harmful to the long-term health of the body? The process of the linking of the virus with its supposed opposite, the immune system, made it extremely difficult to isolate and identify the virus.

As baffling as the quest to identify the virus itself, has been the apparently 'selective' behaviour of Aids as an epidemic. At least in the West, the disease has spread much more quickly in certain groups than in others. This is true, of course, of most epidemics which have spread fastest among the groups directly exposed to a virus, for example, the spread of cholera amongst those using infected water, or the spread of malaria amongst those living closest to malaria-infested swamps. Yet, because the *exact* aetiology of Aids is not yet known, there is much confusion about why it has spread much faster in some groups than in others. Although it is generally agreed that it is in the interchange of bodily fluids like semen and blood that the virus is passed on, it is still not entirely clear why the virus should have spread so much more rapidly among African and Haitian heterosexuals than Western heterosexuals. If conventional medicine had previously wished to concentrate on identifying and suppressing the virus, that approach now appears limited. Even in medical circles, there is a recognition that the control of the disease may well require identifying 'risky' aspects in the host's life style and behaviour just as much as identifying the virus.

Aids is undeniably something of a limit case for conventional medicine. It appears to be contagious in that, in most cases, it is possible to trace the course of the disease and how it was caught. Yet, in so many ways, Aids disrupts existing definitions of a contagious disease and how to 'cure' it. Because of this, conventional medicine has found its very definition of a communicable disease rendered highly ambiguous. For in the past, the definition of a contagious disease was partly dependent on the fact that the virus or bacillus did not discriminate in its transmission, and that the body reacted to the invasion by a harmful organism from the outside. Now allopathic medicine is having to try to understand a process by which the body's immunity turns against itself, leaving the body to be destroyed by other illnesses. And it is having to ask questions about the practices and state of the host which facilitates this process. Conventional medicine has had to question, for the first time, the status of immunity. Instead of an unproblematic ally of health, immunity can no longer be relied on.

No such problems exist for natural therapies. For them, Aids is the prototypical disease of our age. There's an odd way in which they almost predicted the arrival of Aids in the 1970s. As natural therapies gained strength there were increasing warnings that modern life – stress, pollution and life style – were putting at risk immunity and the body's capacity for natural health. A space existed within the philosophies of natural therapies for the arrival of a disease which made visible this heralded collapse of immunity. For, as we have seen in previous chapters, 'immunity' is a central element in alternative philosophies of the body. The alternative health movement is redolent with descriptions of 'weakened immunity status'. There are books with quizzes to test your 'immunity quotient', followed by advice as to how to improve this quotient, one of the main objectives being to acquire 'maximum immunity'. As one advert for a substance to help immunity eloquently put it, 'U.S. Acquires Japanese Defense System'. It is as if the struggle for personal immunity is almost a military or legal struggle against modern life. Indeed immunity had been grafted on to ideas of the natural vitality of self-healing properties of the body as s sort of scientific equivalent. Immunity, or lack of it, are terms which encapsulate the preoccupations of natural medicine, pre-occupations with perfectible health and with a body which is immune, and resistant to disease and death.

While allopathic medicine has scratched its head over such a contrary and apparently selective disease, natural therapies have been quietly proclaiming that they 'told us so'. Aids, we are told, is the quintessential disease of our epoch, a 'modern scourge',[5] foreseen by natural medicine. This total breakdown of all immune function is merely the extreme end of the process of all diseases. 'Aids is the tip of the iceberg in terms of immune diseases, a tragic and awesome tip, and one that has alerted everyone to the necessity of a healthy immune system.'[6] In the eyes of adherents to natural therapies, Aids is both dramatic and definite proof that the population's natural resistance has been under attack, *and* a phenomenon which exposes the limitations, possibly even lies, in the claims made by conventional medicine. Aids can be added by natural therapists to the list of diseases over which modern medicine with its grandoise claims is seen to have failed.

But Aids is also something much more; it is a symbolic illness. It isn't just that conventional medicine hasn't got all the answers. It is also that Aids is seen as symbolic of the general neglect of natural health and immunity and as symbolic of the need for medicines to make 'building up immunity' the first priority for all treatment. For the alternative health movement, Aids is definite proof of many of their fundamental propositions. Not only is it evidence that 'health' depends on the state of an individual's inner vitality but it also shows all too clearly how modern life is putting the health of all at risk. Aids, in short, is far from being a mystery to adherents of alternative approaches to health. For them Aids was inevitable because the stresses of modern life have seriously assaulted our immunity and therefore the capacity of our bodies to stay well. As we have seen earlier this assault is both on our mental and physical well-being, and also at a more general level, the assault of excessive chemical and radioactive output into the atmosphere and pollution of our bodies with the use of synthetic chemicals in food.

In this vision of doom, Aids is like one of the four horsemen of the Apocalypse, heralding the destruction of the earth. Rampant diseases which cannot be controlled are the price a society pays for having destroyed its natural resources at both an individual and a social level.

> Aids, candida, herpes, and cancer are just a few of the diseases which are on the rise precisely during this crucial period of history when the choices we make as human beings are determining the survival of our species and our planet . . . The toxins that have polluted our food, air and water – our means of sustenance – are polluting our bodies and taking their toll. Much of what our parents . . . saw as the cornerstone of their existence upon which they built their lives now seems as fragile as the California coastline. When even apple-pie mix is removed from the grocer's shelf because it may cause cancer, we know we are in trouble. It is no wonder that many of us are sick, or sick with worry. Stress is everywhere.[7]

There is a curious way in which these ideas parallel the more overtly moralistic interpretations of Aids. Here, too, Aids is a sign of something seriously wrong in society.

Victims of allopathic medicine

In this vision of Aids as the symptom of the degeneration of natural health caused by industrial society, one element is often picked out as particularly culpable. This is the use of chemicals in allopathic medicine. It is not just that modern life has attacked our health, there has also been an enemy within. In the very profession which was meant to cure us or keep us well, an enemy has been at work. The use of antibiotics and vaccinations are almost invariably cited as having destroyed our front line of defence against the other attacks of modern life. Culturally, therefore, we have so weakened our overall immunity that there was a certain inevitability that a disease associated with this weakness would appear. Thus, from the point of view of natural therapies, Aids is considerably more than just a come-uppance for the arrogant claims of allopathic medicine; it is actually a Frankenstein loosed from the medical research laboratories.

In the struggle between the external and internal explanations of illness upheld by allopathic and alternative medicine respectively, Aids has been taken as the casting vote. Since what is always crucial for natural therapies is not the disease but the response of the body in fighting off disease, practices like vaccination or excessive use of antibiotics, are viewed as weakenings of the body's own resources, constituting a 'major health hazard' and 'the cause of long-term changes in the immune system and cellular and genetic structure, with unimaginable repercussions in terms of future health'. Thus allopathic medicine is seen as wrong in concentrating on the external 'causes' of illness. 'Much of the thinking behind the concept of giving protection via immunisation stems from the philosophical concept of disease causation which itself requires questioning since it appears to pervert our understanding of the innate self-regulatory mechanisms of the body.'[8]

Those who believe in the internal genesis of illness are also quick to point out that it is possible to reread medical history so that the end of major epidemics can be placed *before* the widespread use of antibiotics and vaccination rather than as a result of it. Overall improvements in health, falling death rates and the end of major epidemics are interpreted as the result of improved hygiene and nutrition rather than any magical medical cures. Easy to see then why the alternative therapies feel none of the surprise of allopathic medicine when faced with Aids. In the natural therapies movement, the virus is neither here nor there; the significant point of any disease – ranging from the common cold, through arthritis to cancer, is the overall well-being of the host. 'If the person's immune system is not compromised . . . they will be able to fight off the virus and not develop the disease.'[9] Thus the great advances of modern medicine are seen as having fatally compromised the ability of the body to fight off disease on its own, through its own inner vitality. Aids becomes symbolic of not only the failure of allopathic medicine to keep us well, but of its part in making us victims to the pressures of modern life.

Since the actual nature of the virus is of little or secondary significance within alternative therapies, what becomes overwhelmingly important is the state of the individual, understood as the state of his or her immune system when he or she encounters a virus. 'The host is seen almost as taking a choice between illness and health. The host, the infected individual and his immune system, decide whether or not Aids (or any other infection) takes hold. The virus or bacteria only play a role if allowed to do so.'[10] In some extreme cases this casts doubt on whether or not there is such a thing as a virus, certainly on whether the virus is more significant than the host's 'choice' in controlling it: 'If you are convinced that Aids . . . is something over which you have no control, then this book is definitely not for you.'[11] Again, Aids emerges as a particularly poignant emblem for alternative approaches to health; the apparently 'selective nature' of the virus is all too easily explained. More than the effect of a virus in destroying immunity, the question becomes inevitably one of why the immunity of certain individuals is so quick to give way.

A psychospiritual illness

The selectivity of the virus which so puzzles conventional medicine is a matter of inevitability for alternative therapies, devoted to the idea of all illness as a sign of inner depletion. Because of this much of the writing on Aids from within alternative therapies has concentrated on why the specific groups most affected by Aids have been so susceptible. Of course, the 'selectivity' of Aids is something promoted by highly repressive and sexually conservative members of society. Aids is seen by these people as 'the gay plague', almost as the judgement of God on a 'perverted' section of society. In this outlook, homosexuality is not only being punished but the whole of society is being made to pay the price for having tolerated homosexuality and perversion for so long. Thus repressive and homophobic commentators inevitably set up a division between those who deserve to be ill and those who they call the 'innocent victims', who have led blameless lives but who have been made to pay the price for society's general wickedness.

These views are clearly not only vicious but crass and stupid, ignoring as they do the pattern of the disease in non-Western countries, not to mention the sexual hypocrisy and general unpleasantness often associated with so-called normal sexual relations. Views on susceptibility from within the natural therapies movement are, by and large, not influenced by such moralistic, normalizing and repressive views of sexuality. Indeed, almost all of the writing on Aids from within alternative therapies is highly sympathetic to the gay community – far more so than many other 'experts' and commentators on Aids. It is no coincidence that so many Aids sufferers have turned to what they call holistic health practices, both because they eschew the pessimism of conventional medicine, and to avoid any apparent moralism about gay life styles. Indeed, in so far as Aids sufferers have received any hope and comfort, it has largely come from alternative therapies.

But in general the emphasis which holistic approaches to health puts on illness as a lack of balance and harmony, still leads to questions as to why a sufferer's life has become unbalanced. It is almost inevitable that, with the emphasis on the integration of mind, emotions and body and on personal responsibility, there is a peculiarly hazy area when it comes to the investigation of the 'deep causes of sickness' in Aids sufferers. There are a number of favoured explanations within the holistic health movement. Most distant from any moralism is the explanation of the gay community as having been particularly susceptible to the attrition caused by the excessive use of antibiotics. The theory, which is in fact widely held, suggests that because venereal diseases were widespread amongst the gay community, gay men have been exposed to high levels of antibiotics. This over-exposure has progressively depleted their natural immune systems, which were therefore already severely depleted when they came into contact with Aids.

In this account, gay men are the particular victims of the undermining of health by the medical profession. However, it is rare to find explanations for the susceptibility of gay men to Aids stopping there. Such explanations are usually integrated into more eleborate explorations of the 'deep imbalances of people with

Aids'.[12] A favoured explanation of these 'deep imbalances' is that along with excessive use of antibiotics, there has been 'excessive' indulgence in sex. Excessive sex is thought to be a problem for two reasons. One is purely 'medical': semen is thought to destroy antibodies as part of the natural process of reproduction when the vagina's instinct to attack harmful invaders is overcome. Thus an 'excessively frequent' receipt of semen is thought to deplete the body's immunity. However, this primarily medical view does sometimes tip into a second set of assumptions about the problems of excessive sex *per se*.

Repeated casual sexual encounters are seen by many involved in the alternative therapies movement as an expression of an inner emptiness, a sign that something is out of balance anyway and therefore a symptom of underlying 'personality' problems which are likely to lead to susceptibility to Aids. 'Many [with Aids] have recognized that, before they became sick, there was a great deal wrong with their lives – not in a moral sense, but quite simply that their day-to-day existence gave little satisfaction and fulfilment, that there was a deep feeling of emptiness in their lives.'[13] This position attempts to distance itself from any moralism about sexual practices: 'Aids is not here to teach us that sex, in particular gay sex is bad. It is here to teach us that sex is an expression of feeling, of our highest selves. If we choose to ignore that and abuse it then it will rebound on us.'[14]

But sometimes this gentler sense of casual sex as an expression of inner loneliness and longing tips into a more ferocious moralism, where it is hard to differentiate views of 'emotional imbalance' from a right-wing attack on a gay life style as a form of perversion:

a deficiency in the immune system seems to be more closely related to the intense stress generated by an anti-life attitude which leaves the individual defenceless in the face of any organic, psychological or spiritual attack . . . Homosexuals and libidinous individuals all have megalomaniac ideas about their sexuality, imagining themselves to be omnipotent, all-powerful and influential. Homosexuals . . . imagine themselves to be new beings, members of a third sex; and this belief obliges them to lie to themselves constantly. Surely this is a profoundly tiring, exhaustive task.[15]

With this interpretation goes a clear call to restructure sexual behaviour, not by having safe sex or by finding new ways of relating sexually, but by restructuring 'our totally erroneous belief that intense sexual activity is necessary for sexual maturity'.[16]

While most views are nothing like as judgemental about sexuality, there is nevertheless a prevalent view that Aids is as much a product of life style as it is of a particular virus. Again and again we encounter this quest to understand what is specific to the affected group's life style and attitudes which has led to their increased susceptibility to Aids:

the holistic health theory sees the attitude as merely setting the stage for susceptibility to disease . . . there are beliefs and attitudes which result in certain behaviours – such as neglecting good nutrition or failing to exercise or simply always maintaining a high level of stress – that predispose an individual to a weakened physical constitution which might lead to the eruption of a condition.[17]

And again, as we have seen in earlier chapters, the privileged explanation for individual susceptibility to illness is stress. It is stress which tips the individual balance of health towards illness, and stress which is the mediator between external assaults and the ability of the individual body to ward off these assaults. Immunity is seen as the barometer of the individual's ability to withstand stress so that the crucial question for alternative therapies is why the particular groups affected by Aids are so much more vulnerable to stress.

The answer provided by one group (the Holistic Group of California) is a relatively 'progressive' one. It concentrates on an explanation of stress as caused by outside pressures on a beleaguered minority rather than the internal pressures of an 'unnatural' life style. Aids is a disease, they say, which takes a particularly strong hold in culturally isolated minorities who experience a very high degree of stress.

We believe that the Aids virus particularly strikes individuals and groups who have been isolated by the dominant culture – culturally isolated minorities who are forced to express their emotional, physical and spiritual nature apart from the community at large – and individuals within those isolated communities who experience undue psychological and/or socioeconomic hardship. Societal isolation places unusually heightened degrees of stress upon the individual and collective mind, body, and spirit of its outcasts. It is this isolation, often internalized as self-hatred or lack of self-acceptance, which allows the Aids virus to begin to incubate once it has entered the system.[18]

As a logical extension of these ideas, there has emerged a belief in the 'psychospiritual nature' of Aids. Aids, we are told, takes root in a community generally weakened by intolerable stresses. The collapse of the immune system is seen as 'connected to the deeper disharmony at the core of this dis-ease, the lack of love from without, internalized as lack of self-love.'[19] And these ideas about the particular stress under which gay men are placed has been extended to encompass other afflicted groups, such as Haitians and Africans. Thus Aids has become a disease of the oppressed.

Many individuals of African origin are raised with a sense of 'cultural castration', with many parallels to that of Haiti, resulting in a depressed sense of self-direction and self-esteem. Africa is a continent so broken up and oppressed by racism and imperialism that attempts on the part of its people to assert independence and autonomy frequently degenerate into military dictatorship which thrive on such psychological and spiritual fragmentation.[20]

I have referred to such views as more progressive by which I mean that at least they 'blame' the disease, not on the victims, but on external causes – political and social oppression. But there's a peculiar opportunism in such ideas; it's not clear, for example, why, if Aids is a disease of an oppressed minority, gay men should be so much more prone to Aids than lesbian women. Nothing in these accounts clarifies why some minorities should be so much more at risk than others. What is more, the tendency to psychologize the disease, and to locate it in life style, is highly problematic. Psychologizing the illness, as we have already seen, is a very definite component of a 'holistic' insistence that disease in the body is connected to mind and emotions. In relation to Aids this tendency takes worrying forms. For, although there is an insistence on the social pressures on gay men, there is the inevitable drift into questions of why some gay men succumb and others do not, and why gay men are more susceptible than other 'minority' groups. The answers are invariably located in accounts of 'the Aids personality'.

Like the cancer personality, the Aids personality is attributed with certain characteristics which 'may make one prone to malignancy. Like cancer and arthritis sufferers, those prone to Aids tend to self-pity. They harbour resentment and have a low self-image. They have difficulty in sustaining long-term relationships.'[21] And since, in the alternative health movement, both cancer and arthritis tend to be related to failures of the immune system, it becomes clear that these are the characteristics most likely to be associated with a failure of immunity. As I have already remarked in Chapter 3, these are hardly characteristics which are widely valued. They imply a person with sexual and social problems, a person whose destructive anger and resentment boils beneath the surface. In the context of the alternative health movement, these characteristics are taken as a sign of a person out of balance, lacking in inner harmony, a person whose unhappiness announces itself in the disease and who is crying out for inner change. By implication the person whose immunity is not at risk is the person who has a conventionally fulfilled life with a stable sexual partner and who is not in conflict with society.

Much of what is said about stress and the gay community clearly makes sense. The push towards the heterosexual norm and so-called normal patterns of 'masculinity' and 'femininity' is obviously intensely destructive and stressful in our culture. But this does not necessarily account for the virulence of a particular disease in a particular community. Nor does it explain why some individuals within the community are more at risk than others. The explanations offered for this in terms of 'psychospiritual afflictions' to which those with certain personalities are prone seems to me to be fraught with dangers, far outweighing the possibility of sympathetic support. For having set up the hypothesis that large numbers of gay men are extremely susceptible to this disease, then there arises the inevitable question of why this particular 'personality' type tends to be found in the gay community. From here it is a small step to extremely simplistic and damaging psychological generalizations about gay men.

Most gay men have a particularly close tie to their mothers, but I have sensed and discovered in a couple of people with Aids, a very powerful mother/child relationship where the person's view of his mother had barely changed since early childhood, i.e. a very passive relationship . . . if an adult is still tied to his or her nurturing parent's 'apron strings', this means he or she is not grounded.[22]

Again, it is clear in the way Aids is being talked about here, that the disease is being firmly attributed to qualities of an individual's life. This emphasis on personal responsibility for health wavers between being supportive and being destructive. It is destructive in the sense that when the individual is in fact no longer able to fight off the disease, he or she is prone to destructive self-analysis and introspection of the 'why am I choosing to let myself die?' kind. Thus the construction of a model where one can 'choose' to be well or ill, leaves enormous problems for the individual who is supposed to be able to make these choices. However sympathetic these ideas may appear to be to the unconscious compulsions which might keep an individual ill, there is an undeniable sense of failure attaching to those who cannnot make it to health.

In the end he did die, but only after he had found a certain peace within himself, making peace with and expressing his feelings to his family and friends. He died because, deep down he made the choice, believing that this was the only way not to have to struggle any more. I respect his choice, although dying is by no means the only way to rise above having to struggle and keep a grip on life.[23]

But there is an odd way in which, if you are seriously ill, it is comforting to come across views which appear to give insights into your own personality and link those with your illness. For, in an era geared up to the idea that we can change our personalities as discussed in Chapter 4, this appears to offer us hope. If conventional medicine cannot cure us, then self-transformation might be able to, and many of the ideas about Aids within alternative therapies offer this message of hope, praising people 'who have used their encounters with Acquired Immune Deficiency as springboards for self-transformation'.[24] Thus there are endless accounts of individuals who speak of Aids as having offered them the chance to transform their lives:

> I had quite a few people think that my initial reaction to my diagnosis was in fact manic, because I saw it as an opportunity . . . Most of the people I know are spiritual people and their reaction was immediately and clearly, 'Oh great, this is gonna be fun! Your life is going to change totally, because what you're doing now with your life is not what you are supposed to be doing. You know it. That's why you've been miserable, that's why you got sick, and this is gonna change it.'[25]

Within the alternative health movement, the work of transformation which individuals with Aids are encouraged to do has become a metaphor for salvation, not just of the individual but for the general work which the whole culture must do for the survival of the planet. Indeed Aids has been transformed into a massive cultural injunction to change, with gay men as the spiritual frontrunners of this change. 'On a global scale Aids is symbolic of the changes, the birth pains that the earth is going through.' Whereas there has never been any success in making cancer seem romantically interesting to those suffering from it (although it could be 'heroic' for those surviving it), the discourses around Aids have managed to carve out a space of spiritual superiority for the sufferers. If they can just die in harmony with themselves, they will be at ease, that is without dis-ease. They will have become the avant-garde of a revolutionary change.

The revolutionary change predicted here is a change in consciousness, with the 'Aids consciousness' (*sic*) viewed as negativity, personal neglect, neglect of the body and nutrition. 'What I believe we are dealing with here is a condition of fear, negativity, guilt and anger that has come to a head. We are being forced to see it in the physical body, that we might begin to learn to grow, to sort out and confront the conditions which we have set up for ourselves at this time.'[26] It seems exceptionally harsh to criticize such views, especially if you know that they are spoken by a masseur who massages those dying with Aids, at a time when they are often brutally ostracized by others in the community. Nevertheless, it is hard not to see such interpretations as symptomatic of a whole push to psychologize and spiritualize illness, making the sick individual an unbalanced individual, and a widespread disease into a spiritual call to arms. There is a very definite outcome anticipated for this revolution. It will be the harmonious, tranquil, 'spiritual' individual, devoid of inner and outer conflict, who is focused on nutrition, exercise and relaxation in pursuit of health.

Conclusions

Aids has provided the alternative health movement with the symptomatic disease *par excellence*. They can argue that Aids is produced by and embodies the horrors of modern industrialized society. But industrial society merely sets the stage for the illness. Actually falling ill with it is to be explained by individual differences, by the strength of our immune systems and, it follows, by the strength of our personality in withstanding stress. The only response to Aids, they tell us, is to transform one's life style and resolve the dis-ease within. In the struggle of gay men to restore health through strengthening their immune systems, we have been given a symbol of new views of health, the body and nature. Aids can be taken as the ultimate sign of the dangers of neglecting nature's healing and restorative ways. For not only is it a disease which conventional medicine cannot 'cure' but it is seen as a disease whereby modern society and modern life styles have attacked and destroyed the body's capacity for natural health.

From this perspective, Aids is seen as the warning which will allow these views of health to get their way. Aids is seen as the stimulus, through the gay community, for the whole population to transform their perceptions of health, and therefore to pursue a truly healthy life style.

It used to be that we only wanted the *image* of good health: tan, glowing skin . . . muscular, well-formed bodies . . . and less specifically an aura of vitality, a certain element of downright sexiness . . . No longer does one hanker for the mere image of health. In so many ways, one is now utterly determined to achieve and keep the real thing . . . the goal now is a deep serenity bred by perfect balance, the peace of mind that manifests itself in a relaxed body and a rich hearty soul.'[27]

Nothing could make clearer the shifts at stake in the discourse around the alternative health movement. The body has a whole new centrality as a place of work and transformation. We are now encouraged to pursue deep health, something quite different and more weighty than the healthy image previously associated with sexuality. Only with deep health will we be truly immune, exempt from attacks of illness and untouchable by the stresses and strains of modern life. And our minds and emotions are described as being ultimately in control of these transformations; it is up to us to make the choice to be well and that choice will be reflected in the state of our immunity.

Significantly sexuality has been displaced in this push towards a new goal of true health or well-being. And the arguments that gay sexual mores should be transformed in favour of pursuing deep health are certainly symptomatic of general shifts from sexuality to health. Indeed it is clear that illness (with Aids as the ultimate illness) now carries the weight of personal morality previously carried by decisions about sexual behaviour. After all, well-being is only gained through the hard work of transformation, a shedding of 'negative' attitudes and behaviours. For the ill person this means the transformation of the 'deep imbalances of one's life'; it means making a 'choice' to be healthy and altering one's life style accordingly. For the 'worried well', it means the relentless pursuit of maximum immunity, a pursuit of the body which speaks of an inner wholesomeness and well-being.

Commentators might wish to shift any moral 'blame' away from those who become ill but the general implications of all this are unavoidably moralistic, even if not in conventional ways. Aids is the symbol of failure, and neglect, of internalized weakness. And our susceptible bodies are signs of our own internalization of the corrupting values of surrounding culture. It is a curious reversal of the shocking moralism of sexual conservatives who blame Aids on the 'corrupt' life style of homosexual men. But the reversal occupies the same terrain. For in both, the disease has a meaning; it is trying to speak of something wrong in the state of the individual. For the sexual conservatives the individual is to blame; he or she is just a bad person. In alternative therapies the individual is more likely to be a victim, a victim of modernity gone too far. Yet the individual can 'choose' to be well again and the existence of that choice tends to imply the 'strength' and heroism of those who make it to the other side. It seems as if these moralistic views of illness have never been able to let go, that they have resurfaced in another form, as 'psychospiritual' diseases. And Aids has provided the clearest focus for these views.

Notes

1 Serinus, *Psychoimmunity and the Healing Process*.
2 ibid.
3 Sontag, op. cit.
4 Allan M. Brandt, *No Magic Bullet*.
5 Leon Chaitow, *Vaccination and Immunization*.
6 Serinus, op. cit.
7 ibid.
8 Chaitow, op. cit.
9 Dr Jay Levy, *Time* magazine, 3 November 1986.
10 Chaitow, op. cit.
11 Nick Bamforth, *Aids and the Healer Within*.
12 ibid.
13 ibid.
14 ibid.
15 Pacheco, op. cit.
16 ibid.
17 Paul Reed, *Serenity. Challenging the Fear of Aids*.
18 Serinus, op. cit.
19 ibid.
20 ibid.
21 Carl Simonton et al., *Getting Well Again*.
22 Bamforth, op. cit.
23 ibid.
24 Serinus, op. cit.
25 ibid.
26 Article by I. Smith in Serinus, op. cit.
27 Reed, op. cit.

Conclusion – The Wholesome Entrepreneur

In this book I have been describing the emergence of a series of connected beliefs about health and the body. It is undoubtedly the case that alternative therapies have become popular not just because they offer a more caring approach to health than conventional medicine but also because they correspond to, perhaps even spearhead, these changed views. Clearly people's expectations of health, and their sense of personal involvement in it have changed. So too have beliefs about how much they can exercise conscious 'choice' over health and disease. Even the conception of disease has changed: disease is no longer understood either as the curse of mankind or as a completely arbitrary phenomenon. Instead disease and well-being are both seen as having direct personal 'meanings'. And through the notion of holism, with its implicit privileging of the mind over the body, the 'meaning' of disease is more often than not located in the individual's state of mind.

In the preceding chapters we have seen how these changed beliefs rely on a philosophy whose central tenets are the beneficial, healing powers of nature, natural energies, the possibility and desirability of the whole person, and the importance of attending to the inner 'ecology' of the body, primarily through the medium of food. Interest in alternative therapies rarely stops at using one particular therapy to deal with an ailment when allopathic medicine has failed. The interest invariably extends into a wholehearted adoption of these philosophical concepts. In looking at these concepts, I have attempted to unpick their component parts, to place them in relation to social forces and to question some of their assumptions. Yet certain general questions still remain and require some kind of answer. Why exactly have beliefs about the body and health changed and what is it that these new philosophies appear to satisfy? Why are they so popular? To answer these questions involves pulling out the recurrent themes of this philosophy and trying to understand their appeal.

One simple answer is that alternative therapies make explicit – and give a theory to – the absolute centrality which the body and health have acquired in our consciousness. Attending to health and well-being has become a major cultural obsession and alternative therapies satisfy something of the sense that we should be 'committed' to our bodies and our health; they cater for the sense that even 'the worried well' should be doing something definite for their health. This new commitment to the body's well-being is far from nebulous; it involves a new sense of the body. Our knowledge of the body has been infinitely extended. We now have before us a whole inner geography, an inner ecology to which we must attend by changing our diets, our posture, and even our attitudes. To some extent commentators are right when they attribute this new and detailed concern with the body's health to the 'privileges' of a society which has high standards of living and hygiene so that it can both permit such introspection and contemplate a society without disease. But the concern is also something far more.

This new concern with the body is a place where people can express dissatisfaction with contemporary society *and* feel they are doing something personally to resist the encroachments of that society. Indeed, so strong is the sense of social criticism in this health movement that many adherents proclaim they are the avant-garde of a quiet social revolution. Yet the journey to this social revolution is rarely a journey towards social rebellion but more often an inner journey, a journey of personal transformation. The quest for natural health has come to be the focus of a new morality where the individual is encouraged to exercise personal control over disease. And the principal route to this control is the route to a 'changed consciousness' and changed life style. With this emphasis on changing consciousness have come all the fantasies and projections associated with religious morality, fantasies of wholeness, of integration and of the individual as origin of everything good or bad in their life. And with these fantasies there has mushroomed the industry of 'humanistic psychotherapies' emphasizing the role of the individual will-power in making changes.

There is nothing particularly new about the body being the focus of a personal morality in Western societies. But previously it was through sexuality that individuals were required to look into themselves, make decisions about how to use their body and find their true worth. It was around sexual behaviour that erstwhile religious concepts like guilt, sin, self-denial and joy continued to live on in the person. And it was in sexuality and sexual behaviour that the individual was called upon to exercise the greatest degree of self-determination, to make choices about behaviour. In the Victorian period this took the form of exercising restraint, of controlling degrading 'natural' impulses; in the latter half of the twentieth century, it was increasingly a question of exploring possibilities in order to discover the truth about oneself, of putting oneself more in touch with 'natural' impulses. Although this latter period might appear less moralistic, it is nevertheless the flip side of the Victorian era. It is still a question of the use of the body as 'proof', to demonstrate the inner personality.

But in the last decade or so, sexuality as proof has been gradually nudged aside. Increasingly, health is the place where this personal morality is located. It is increasingly the state of our health which will reveal the truth about our inner being and our relation to 'nature'. That health should have become so important and brought with it 'moral' concerns previously located in sexuality, seems to be due to a conjunction of various social forces over the last twenty years. Firstly, there is quite simply the increasing instability of sexuality as a focus for 'moral discourse'. Even if the response to Aids represents a sexual backlash, no one could possibly deny the major and apparently irreversible changes which have taken place in sexual attitudes. There is no longer any agreed sexual morality; it has become a contested place. Significant in the rupture of moral certainty about sex have been three factors – the breakdown of Christian morality as the dominant 'ethos' of society, the changing position of women, and the availability of contraception. The outcome is a situation where the possibilities for sexual connection are far more fluid, and where individuals do not have to confine sexual connection within marriage. And such have been the changes that it is almost unimaginable that sexuality could ever again be fully contained within a moral hegemony. Few and far between are the individuals whose own personal life or family have been untouched by the changing patterns of sexual connection.

It might be asked why there should be any morality about the body if sexuality has become increasingly unstable as a focus. Why should moral categories have regrouped around health? But it is clearly difficult for a society like ours to abandon the moral categories of Christianity and especially to abandon the requirement that an individual should 'prove' his or her worth through exercising some control over their body. Even though the contemporary health movement emphasizes the integration of body and mind there can be little doubt that these new attitudes conceal a morality where the individual is meant to 'choose' between positive and negative states, right and wrong. The morality may not be very obvious. It is not after all a case of prescriptions as to what we should or should not do. Even so, the contemporary health movement is riddled with the dualism which so typifies Christian views of morality. Instead of good and evil we now have the oppositions between modern society and nature, between disease and health. These two forces carry all the attributes previously located in the terms 'good' and 'evil'. To pursue a natural life style and diet is to find yourself on the side of the 'whole', the integrated, balanced and healing forces of nature. Above all, it is to be on the side of the 'healthy'. To ignore natural laws is to side with the fragmented, the inharmonious, with modern 'mass' society, with junk, technology and destruction. Ultimately it is an alliance with disease. The individual must choose between these forces, between the life-giving forces of nature and the destructive forces of the modern world. And the sign of the choice we make is 'health'. The opposition between health and disease is a profound opposition between wholeness and fragmentation, between conflict and peace.

But why should individuals, recently freed from the sense of damnation which surrounded them in religion or in sexuality, immediately succumb to a new philosophy in which the body is seen to express their personal will? The answer lies precisely in the term which I have just used. Personal will. We live in a society which believes that the individual is responsible for his or her actions and indeed that the individual is ultimately responsible for whatever happens to her in society, whether she succeeds or fails.

This is the legacy of Protestant Christianity with its belief that the salvation of the individual depends on his or her own actions. And these views are still deeply held by our society even though organized religion does not appear to dominate our consciousness. Conservative politicians may try and convince us that society has been weakened by socialist theories which let individuals off the hook by 'blaming' the structure of society for social ills. But the fact is that 'moralistic' views of the individual have never really been shaken. The revival of political Conservatism in Britain merely gave new life to these views which remain the dominant personal ethics in Western societies.

There had been a moment in the early 1970s when, intellectually at least, there was a serious challenge to this ethic of the free individual responsible for his or her own fate. In the wake of Freud many people were prepared to consider that the individual was riven by unconscious contradictions, and that the possibility of changing our life by an effort of will was an illusion. What is more, Marxist-influenced ideas which located the ills of society firmly in the social structure were enjoying a temporary prevalence. These argue that whole classes of people are structurally disadvantaged in a society based on competition for resources and the control of resources in the hands of a few. Although these ideas never gained ascendancy there was nevertheless a growth in state services – education, health, and services for the elderly and the disabled – where society seemed to acknowledge a sense of *social* responsibility, a sense that it was not simply up to individuals to secure their fate. But by the end of the 1970s those new departures were well under attack. Conservative politics were able to take up and articulate all the social problems of the day and blame them on the 'nanny state' and the breakdown of the sense of individual responsibility for their actions. Political Conservatism gave new wind to the idea of individuals as entirely in control of their actions and responsible for their good or bad fortune.

What happened to medicine and attitudes towards health seems symptomatic of what happened at a more general political level. Several criticisms of conventional medicine converged, criticisms which were then hegemonized by a new philosophy of the body and personal responsibility. Conventional medicine in the post-war period was ripe for criticism. There was a growing awareness of the 'inhumanity' of conventional health care. Increasingly people realized that some of the major events of life – birth, illness and death – have been horrendously mismanaged in a society where status and profit predominated. People have found themselves caring for sick and dying relatives and friends without support from the medical profession. Perhaps medical institutions actively contributed to the horrors of illness and loss. Increasingly the attitudes of male professionalism have seemed outrageously at odds with a supposedly caring profession. At the same time, conventional medicine carried a message that disease and illness were arbitrary, having no meaning in terms of the quality of an individual's life. For the first time in Western history disease was firmly separated from any moral or religious discourse. It seems likely that this separation of disease from the 'will of God' or the 'sins of humanity' created a distinct unease for a society steeped in religious beliefs of disease.

These two developments in conventional medicine are not in fact necessarily connected with each other. Allopathic medicine is based on philosophies of the external causality of illness. There is no *necessity* that such a philosophy should produce impersonality in care, and a disregard of people in favour of profit. It is probably true that this belief has tended to direct research towards viral and bacterial illness. And this direction means that certain knowledges of the body, knowledge for example of the bones and muscles, have been shamefully neglected. So it should come as no surprise that alternative therapies have their most visible successes with manipulation of bones and muscles. But the inhumanity of the medical profession doesn't arise directly out of the notion of disease in allopathic medicine. This inhumanity is much more likely to be explained by the professional hierarchies, the unequal division of labour between men and women, the prevalence of professional attitudes, and the pursuit of profit by pharmaceutical companies. Yet these two elements were seen by many as one and the same thing. Indeed exponents of alternative medicine often blame conventional medicine's inhumanity on the fact that it refuses to see the connection between illness and the individual's life.

What happened with alternative medicine was symptomatic of what happened in many areas of society at the same moment. People blamed everything that was wrong on 'materialism', on philosophies which argued that individuals were not responsible for the good and evil that befell them. Thus, instead of criticizing the structures of work, or the failures and neglects of conventional medicine, there evolved a full-scale attack on the way personal responsibility for health has been down-played. Alternative therapies came to be viewed as something more than complementing or supplementing the failures of allopathic medicine. They became a place for a new philosophy of personal responsibility. As with other social developments, lack of personal responsibility became an easy way of describing all the complicated reasons why institutions and practices have evolved in certain ways. Rather than a historical or political analysis of why things had gone wrong, it was easy to blame 'materialism'. And when alternative therapies did look for a history or a theory, they sometimes found it in a simplistic feminism, which divided the world into feminine and masculine principles with conventional medicine 'explained' by the dominance of male, materialist, technological values.

Many practitioners of alternative medicine will doubtless be angered to find themselves linked to conservative views of society. For them the movement is giving voice to a discontent with the social status quo. They see *allopathic* medicine as part of the conservative forces which have been so contemptuous of nature with their defence of individual rights to exploit resources in the pursuit of profit. And it is undoubtedly the case, as I have already said, that one of the main attractions of alternative medicine is that it clearly articulates a widespread sense that there is something very wrong with society. Whether in connection with food or psychotherapy, or just on views of nature and natural health, there are always criticisms of the impersonality of modern technical society and the damage it does. Yet, as I have repeatedly stressed throughout this book, these criticisms almost invariably slide towards a polarization between the generalizations of 'the modern' on one hand and 'nature' on the other. It is rare for these criticisms to join up with a more thoroughgoing challenge to the structures of a capitalist society. A sense of social powerlessness is expressed as hatred of the machine.

Frequently the criticism of society expressed in alternative therapies turns into a nostalgia for an imagined wholeness and health, for what has been destroyed by modern society. This opposition between nature and modern society is hardly a new one. In past periods nature has similarly featured as a term permitting a nostalgia for something lost and a critique of existing society – perhaps a lost innocence as with the Romantic poets, or a lost sense of sexual spontaneity as in the 1960s. Now it signifies a lost wholeness and health. And the criticisms of society can be deduced from all those attributes which are set up as the opposite of nature. In the alternative health movement, nature is none of the following things: it is not technological, scientific, rationalist; not industrial; it is not fragmented, arbitrary and without meaning; it knows nothing of bad posture, bad parenting, bad diet; above all, it knows nothing of disease. Clearly the critique of modern society is a very limited one. It focuses on the corruptions of the modern world and their effect of causing the body to degenerate. Indeed the fear of degenerative diseases seems of overwhelming significance as if the worst thing to be said about modern society is that we are ill, and that this can be blamed on the lack of control individuals have over their bodies.

The health of the body, achieved through the healing processes outlined in this book, is presented as the vital front line by which the individual can counter the excesses of 'modernity', of 'industrialization' and impersonality. Becoming healthy has become synonymous with finding 'nature' and 'a natural life style' and this is to be the route by which advanced industrial society will be resisted. The resistance does not rest on an analysis of social structures, of social divisions, of unequal control of resources. Instead it is a vision of personal resistance, of making oneself 'immune' to modern life. The alternative health movement has become a place where the individual can play out, in a highly personal way, a sense of the corruptions of modernity and the struggle against these corruptions. Now the corruptions are no longer the religious sins of greed, sex, and envy, nor the economic sins of capitalism but rather bad parenting, bad diet, bad posture, the abuse of food and nature. The solutions to these are rarely political. They are individual. It is up to individuals to transform themselves, to deal with the pain and suffering imposed by modern life.

Some would want to argue that these views of the corruptions of the world derive from very real political fears: fears of the impersonality of bureaucracy, and fears of the obliteration of ourselves and the planet earth by techological developments which appear out of our control. From this perspective, the reinstatement of individual responsibility is both a symptom (of that general sense of powerlessness) and a necessity, a new stage of personal politics. Until individuals assume responsibility for their bodies and counter the forces making them ill, then there is no hope for wider transformations. But this explanation is by no means sufficient. The sense of the corruptions of the world is too symbolic and personalized to derive exclusively from internalized political fears. These ideas of the corruptions of the world are the direct inheritors of relgous dualities between the corruption of the material world, and the perfectibility of the individual, even if this perfectibility is now played out in relation to the body rather than the soul, and in relation to the here and now rather than the afterlife. Even the fears of the destruction of our planet sometimes have a millenarian inflection – if we can save ourselves, we can save the planet.

It is clear, too, that the emphasis on personal responsibility rarely generates political empowerment. It may generate a sense of being able to accomplish things within the existing status quo, but it rarely promises the ability to transform social structures. The crucial aim in all this work is that the individual should feel better, less in conflict and less dragged down by the horrors of modern life. The rewards of this are very often rather paradoxical. The individual will be able to do better, achieve more, and live in greater ease in this society. Very often the aims are almost explicitly conservative. They are aims of harmony, order, balance, the end of struggle, strife, and 'unproductive' conflict. The possibility that there are very real objective interests governing the form of society in which we live is erased in these aims. The healed individual is one who can have and be everything in the existing society. Small wonder then that the 'type' I met most often while researching this book was the wholesome entrepreneur, the perfect resolution of a personal politics of the body with a peaceful co-existence within the existing economic structure.

It is a potential misrepresentation of alternative therapies to concentrate on the philosophies of personal resolution. Many people within the alternative therapies movement are concerned in active ways with anti-nuclear and ecological politics. And it would also be extremely foolish to challenge some of the hopes of this health movement. Who wants to be miserable and in conflict, and possibly even ill, if you can feel well and contented? And what's wrong with starting with the individual and then looking for wider social changes based on a community of changed individuals? The problem is that the aspirations of self-transformation are rarely limited just to feeling in optimum good health or empowered. To achieve this state of well-being the individual will have to transform his or her personality. And this transformation has very definite goals, the individual without conflict, the individual who is no longer up in arms about society, the individual who has expressed and got rid of anger and envy, the emotions which might lead her or him into conflict with society. You will only be well if you can achieve this emotional state. This is truly the route of being 'alternative', for alternative implies co-existing with existing structures not challenging them. And action simply becomes a matter of personal choice between two routes, rather than a matter of creating a different society with different values.

Bibliography

Balaskas, Janet, *Active Birth*, New York, McGraw Hill, 1983

Bamforth, Nick, *Aids and the Healer Within*, New York, Amethyst Books, 1987

Bandler, Richard and John Grinder, *Frogs into Princes: Neuro Linguistic Programming*, Moab, Ut., Real People Press, 1970

Benjamin, Harry, *Everybody's Guide to Nature Cure*, North Hollywood, Ca., Newcastle Publications, 1982

Birkinshaw, Elyse, *Turn Off Your Age*, Santa Barbara, Ca., Woodbridge Press, 1980

Brandt, Allan M., *No Magic Bullet: A History of Venereal Disease in the United States Since 1880*, New York, Oxford University Press, 1985

Brook, Danae, *Naturebirth: Preparing for Natural Birth in an Age of Technology*, London, Heinemann, 1985

Chaitow, Leon, *Vaccination and Immunization, Dangers, Delusions and Alternatives*, Saffron Walden, C. W. Daniel, 1987

Connolly, Christopher and Hetty Einzig, *The Fitness Jungle*, London, Century, 1986

Course in Miracles, A, London, Arkana, 1985

Donnison, Jean, *Midwives and Medical Men*, London, Heinemann, 1977.

Dossey, Larry, *Beyond Illness: Discovering the Experience of Health*, London, Shambhala, 1985

Ehrenreich, Barbara and Deirdre English, *Witches, Midwives and Nurses: A History of Women Healers*, New York, Feminist Press, 1986

Gawain, Shakti, Creative Visualization, New York, Bantam, 1982

Gawler, Ian, *You Can Conquer Cancer: A Self-help Guide to the Way Back to Health*, Wellingborough, Thorsons, 1986

Gerras, Charles (ed.), *Feasting on Raw Foods: Over 350 Healthy No-cook Recipes*, Wellingborough, Thorsons, 1986

Greenwald, Jerry, *Be the Person You Were Meant to Be*, New York, Dell, 1973

Griffin, Susan, *Woman and Nature: The Roaring Inside Her*, New York, Harper and Row, 1978

Harris, Thomas A., *I'm OK – You're OK*, London, Pan, 1973

Harrison, John, *Love Your Disease*, London, Angus and Robertson, 1984

Horn, Sandra, *Relaxation: A Self-help Guide to the Prevention and Control of Stress-related Illness*, Wellingborough, Thorsons, 1986

Hulke, Malcolm (ed.), *The Encyclopedia of Alternative Medicine and Self Help*, New York, Schocken, 1979

Inglis, Brian and Ruth West, *The Alternative Health Guide*, London, Michael Joseph, 1983

Kenton, Leslie and Susannah, *Raw Energy: Eat Your Way to Radiant Health*, London, Century Arrow, 1986

Krystal, Phyllis, *Cutting the Ties that Bind*, Los Angeles, Ca., Aura Enterprises, 1982

Laut, Phil, *Money is My Friend*, Cincinnati, Ohio, Trinity Publications, 1979

Lindsay, Norman, *My Mask: for what little I know of the man behind it*, London, Angus and Robertson, 1970

Livingstone, Ronald, *Healthy Living in a Polluted World*, Lebanon, Ky., The Cedar Press, 1973

Mandell, Earl, *Shaping Up with Vitamins*, Arlington, Va., Arlington Books, 1985

McKinlay, John B. (ed.), *Issues in the Political Economy of Health Care*, London, Tavistock, 1985

Mendelsohn, Robert S., *How to Raise a Healthy Child in spite of Your Doctor*, Chicago, Contemporary Books, 1984

Moule, Tom, *Nature Cure in a Nutshell: The Simple Guide to Healthful Living*, London, Health for All Publishing, 1953

Odent, Michel, *Birth Reborn: What Birth Can and Should Be*, London, Souvenir Press, 1984

Orr, Leonard and Sondra Ray, *Rebirthing in the New Age*, Berkeley, Ca., Celestial Arts, 1977

Pacheco, Claudia Bernhardt, *Healing Through Consciousness*, New York, Proton Editora, 1983

Pietroni, Patrick, *Holistic Living: A Guide to Self Care*, London, J. M. Dent, 1986

Pleshette, Janet, *Cures That Work: A Comprehensive Guide to Alternative Medicines That Really Work*, London, Century Arrow, 1986

Reed, Paul, *Serenity. Challenging the Fear of Aids*, Berkeley, Ca., Celestial Arts, 1986

Ritson, Christopher, et al. (eds.), *The Food Consumer*, Chichester, John Wiley, 1986

Rowan, John, *A Guide to Humanistic Psychology*, Publication of the Association for Humanistic Psychology, 1987

Serinus, Jason (ed.), *Psychoimmunity and the Healing Process: A Holistic Approach to Immunity and Aids*, Berkeley, Ca., Celestial Arts, 1986

Simonton, Carl, et al., *Getting Well Again*, New York, Bantam, 1980

Sontag, Susan, *Illness as Metaphor*, New York, Farrar, Straus and Giroux, 1978

Spretnak, Charlene, *The Politics of Women's Spirituality: Essays on the Rise of Spiritual Power Within the Feminist Movement*, New York, Doubleday, 1982

Thurston, Emory W., *The Parent's Guide to Better Nutrition for Tots and Teenagers*, New Canaan, Ct., Keats Publishing, 1979

Valentine, Tom and Carole, *Medicine's Missing Link: Metabolic Typing and Your Personal Food Plan*, Wellingborough, Thorsons, 1987

Vaughan, Frances, *The Inward Arc: Healing and Wholeness in Psychotherapy and Spirituality*, London, Shambhala, 1985

Warren-Clarke, Ly, *The Way of the Goddess: A Manual for Wiccan Initiation*, New York, Avery Publications, n.d.

Weiner, Michael A., *Maximum Immunity: How to Fortify Your Natural Defences Against Cancer, AIDS, Arthritis, Allergies And Other Deficiency Diseases*, Bath, Gateway Books, 1986

Well-Being, Channel 4 Publications, London, 1984

Index